Human Evolution, D...
The Case for Palaeolithic Nutrition
By Mark Hines

Healthy Body Publishing
www.thehealthybodyco.com

Logo by Leonardo Solano:
www.leonardosolano.com
New Media & Communications

Copyright © 2008 by Mark Hines

A Healthy Body Publishing Book
0-9553800

Printed in England by Antony Rowe Limited

First published in 2009 as a Health Body Publishing paperback
London, United Kingdom

ISBN: 978-0-9553800-2-0

For information regarding permission to reproduce any material from
this book, contact www.thehealthybodyco.com

The Author

Mark Hines is an Exercise and Human Physiologist, based at the British College of Osteopathic Medicine, London, England. He writes and teaches private courses on exercise, nutrition and the palaeolithic diet, and has written various books and articles on related subjects for a wide variety of readers. In his spare time he competes in ultra-endurance adventure races around the world.

Acknowledgements

I would like to thank all of the people that read the draft manuscripts and contributed to the shaping of this edition. I am sure that your suggestions and feedback have made this publication far superior to what it would have been without you. Thanks to Dr Caroline Walker, Lysbeth O'Sullivan, Mike Topping, Mckenzie Sager, John Quinn, Stuart Locke, Sarah Cocks, Lucy Armstrong, Eddie Griffith, Dr Oliver Mytton, Dr Simon Dyall, and Ross Hanbury. I would particularly like to thank Rose Drew for being such an enormous help in checking details and assisting with research.

Dedication

To Rose Drew,
for all your invaluable help and support

Disclaimer

This book has been written to give an insight into the currently available evidence of our evolution and the conflicts between our genotype and modern diets. The information contained is not to be taken as prescriptive, and should not be interpreted as such, particularly in place of advice given on an individual basis by an appropriately qualified health-care professional.

Contents

V

VI

"It would be a waste of effort to gather, in order to convince the doubters, still more evidence that man has evolved. Their doubts come not so much from lack of knowledge as from resistance to knowledge. That man, like other biological species, is a product of evolution, is now platitudinous"

– Dobzhansky, 1972 [35].

Forward

As human beings we often pride ourselves on what we perceive as our superiority over the rest of the animal kingdom. We view our accomplishments as a species in terms of our homes and societies, our enjoyment of culture, literature and the arts, and our great technological advances. Whilst some primates and other animals use crude tools in their everyday life, we have taken tool use to the extremes. Our technology provides our transport, our home comforts, our entertainment, our medicine and our travel.

We do not necessarily regard ourselves purely in terms of our intellect, but of our consciousness as well. We can define ourselves within various social groups, according to where we are from, where we work, our beliefs, language, skin colour, IQ, status, politics, and so on. We exist as one species, and yet we divide ourselves, not least into countries, societies, communities and religions. Because we are reluctant to see ourselves as part of a whole, we have wars and spend great fortunes funding those wars, whilst our brothers and sisters in other parts of the world are suffering from famine. At some point we have to accept that whilst our technology and consciousness create a lot of convenience for us, it does not necessarily imply that we are a particularly selfless species (perhaps none are, but the point was to assess any justification for our self-appointed superiority over the rest of the animal kingdom). At some point, we have to accept that our reliance and faith in technology, might allow us to overlook the possibility that it does have its pitfalls (both globally and individually). Unless we learn about such pitfalls and make informed choices accordingly, then there are many ways in which we might be sacrificing our health and longevity.

As individuals, what repercussions are there for us, resulting from our current Space Age lifestyles? Why is it that the westernised countries are the ones with the highest incidences of diabetes, heart disease, and obesity? A third of cancers are related to nutritional shortcomings, so why is it that the richest countries are the ones suffering? Surely the technology should be in place to prevent these common diseases of affluence, especially in countries where individuals have sufficient money to be able to exercise their preferences, particularly in preventative measures?

Medical research, to all intents and purposes, is making swift gains in developing better methods of detection and treatment. But public health faces an uphill struggle. Our technology is advanced enough to sustain us as a species, but it does so while reducing our health. This, in turn, has serious repercussions for those of us who want to lose weight and/or prevent the onset of various diseases. If the body is harbouring a sub-clinical nutrient deficiency, then reducing food intake to facilitate weight loss is going to exacerbate the level of deficiency. Hence, most weight loss strategies do not work in the long-term, simply because the diet is too unhealthy in the first instance. Nobody seems to realise this.

Likewise, there is conflicting information regarding the prevention of modern diseases. The problem is often that the recommendations are made in the light of the type of foods that most commonly surround us today. In nature, when conflict occurs between a species and its environment, then the species either adapts or it becomes extinct. Whilst we have the technology to preserve our species despite our growing conflict with nature, on an individual basis we are the ones that may one-day have to depend upon pharmaceuticals, suffer poor mental and physical health, and experience decreased life-expectancy. Furthermore, as this burden grows in our ageing societies, so the economical burden will reach the government and then will no doubt be reflected back onto us (particularly for those of us in a welfare state where taxes translate to employment benefits, healthcare and pensions).

The purpose of this book, therefore, is to demonstrate how our genotype (the collection of genes that make us human) is in conflict with our modern lifestyles, and how this conflict results in modern disease and obesity. Thus, the key to improved health, and the prevention of obesity and modern disease, can be found in the resolution of this conflict. In terms of health in general, both psychological and environmental stresses are also involved, but these areas are too diverse to be included within the scope of research for this book. What will be shown, however, is that various nutrients are involved in maintaining mental health and limiting the damage from environmental pollutants.

Einstein once said: *"I do not know with what weapons World War Three will be fought, but World War Four will be fought with sticks and stones."*

On the assumption that we should not be waiting for the aftermath of WWIII to resolve the conflict between our modern selves and our Stone Age genotype, we are fortunate that science has presented us with another solution. Modern technology is developing the means to sustain the growing global population of our species more efficiently than ever before. Meanwhile, the world of medicine is developing to more effectively stem the rising incidences of modern disease and obesity that currently afflicts our species.

Darwinian Medicine relates how our genotype evolved over millions of years, to how our health has declined since civilisation and global population expansion took hold. The keys to better health, less disease, and less obesity can be found by understanding how our species has moved away from the environment in which it evolved, and *ergo* the environment to which it was genetically most suited. Perhaps with time, the study of human evolution will become an integral feature of modern medicine.

A healthier and more svelte global population is surely the image to best suit our Space Age lifestyles. But thanks to science, we do not have to rely on technology to make up for our shortcomings, nor to several visits to G.P. surgeries, the pharmacy, and/or the operating theatre. Thanks to our improved understanding of our place in nature, from the studies of human evolution and all of the sciences that surround it, we can understand that the resolution of conflict lies not in the hands of technology, but in a simple understanding of our past. Now is the time to use our current understanding of the human body and our place in nature, to bring our state of being back around full circle.

A Short History of Medicine:

2000 B.C. - Here, eat this root.
1000 A.D. - That root is heathen. Here, say this prayer.
1850 A.D. - That prayer is superstition. Here, drink this potion.
1940 A.D. - That potion is snake oil. Here, swallow this pill.
1985 A.D. - That pill is ineffective. Here, take this antibiotic.
2000 A.D. - That antibiotic is artificial. Here, eat this root.

- **Author Unknown**

XII

Introduction

A Whirlwind Introduction to Evolution by Natural Selection, and the Fate of Humankind

"Sometimes I think the surest sign that Intelligent Life exists elsewhere in the Universe is that none of it has tried to contact us."
- Bill Watterson

Those that have studied, in any reasonable depth, the evolution of life on this planet should be amazed by all of the organisms that surround us. Taking exception to those that believe in the Intelligent Design hypothesis, Darwinian natural selection describes how each species is the best adapted to its environment, by comparison to other species that try to fill the same ecological niche. That is to say that across the entire history of life on Earth, each species has been able to out-compete its competitors and therefore be the most successful in its environment. That success is due to a combination of factors related to what that particular species eats, how much it eats, how quickly it reproduces, how many offspring it has each time, how long it lives and how effectively it avoids predation. For that 'successful' species to continue to exist through time, it must only be better adapted than its competitors, and then the species itself must be able to adapt to new environments that are presented to it over time. Evolution does not *design* an organism to be the greatest possible eventuality for a particular environment. In order to survive, the organism needs only to be better adapted than its rivals, or perhaps nothing more than the *least worst*.

Over the course of life's history on this planet, the climate has changed, ice ages have come and gone (and come again), global temperatures have soared and plummeted, and sea levels and continents have shifted. The point of this rather brief and simplistic review of evolution and natural selection is simple: the ancestors of

7

all the species that are alive now were the best possible species for their environments. That is how they came to thrive and to have offspring that eventually evolved into the life that surrounds us today. They were not simply some halfway point between a crude and primitive form, and a better and more advanced form that exists today; they were absolutely the best form for their environment and ecological niche. If the species of today were exchanged with those of a hundred million years ago, then many would become extinct through a lack of specialisation, because any given species has adapted so completely to the environment in which it lives.

There are various exceptions to this rule, such as the speciation that occurs following a mass extinction event, in which vast swathes of life-forms are driven to extinction, either during the event or in its aftermath. For example, it was the extinction of the dinosaurs some 65 million years ago that allowed the mammals to diversify and become what they are today, you and I included. Had that mass extinction event not occurred, then we would not be here, although some descendents of the *mammalia* might be, along with some very different looking dinosaurs (birds are their current living descendants). It is also true that some classes of organisms, such as the crocodilians, have remained relatively unchanged for over 200 million years. This is on account of their line never being adequately challenged by anything else, regardless of changing environments and so on (although it is fair to say that plenty of crocodilians would have died out in particular areas, but many species survived well enough still to be highly successful to this day). Thus, everything that is alive today is alive because there has not been a single break in the history of its evolution, going back to the last common ancestor of everything alive on Earth. Every living thing has ancestors that have been the best adapted for their environments, and that avoided annihilation from predation and mass extinction. The life that currently exists on Earth represents less than a single percentage of all the life that has ever existed, or that could be in existence today. The fact that we are here at all, particularly with our ability to read and write and to enjoy literature and the arts, is even more amazing.

What we need to ask ourselves, however, is whether or not our 'great' intellects; our inventions and our innovations, could in any way be responsible for our downfall. The existence of human beings on Earth contributes to such an insignificant amount of time in the context of all of life's history, that it is incredible how one species has achieved so much (good, bad and indifferent). Yet, despite the brevity of our time on the planet, our current way of living represents less than one percent of our total existence as a species. Did our swelling brains, so important for allowing our species to adapt and survive, facilitate the current trend in our species to be so susceptible to becoming overweight, so weak and liable to disease (such as heart disease, diabetes, various cancers and Alzheimer's disease)? It is our advantage as a species to be able to understand our fate, should current trends continue unabated, and it is our privilege to be able to intervene consciously to have a positive affect our own futures.

"A human being is a part of the whole called by us 'the universe,' a part limited in time and space. He experiences himself, his thoughts and feelings, as something separate from the rest — a kind of optical delusion of consciousness. This delusion is a kind of prison for us, restricting us to our personal desires and the affection of a few persons nearest to us. Our task must be to free ourselves from this prison by widening our circle of understanding and compassion to embrace all living creatures and the whole of nature in its beauty."

- Albert Einstein

We are the result of thousands of millions of years of life on Earth. This fact is not so much a validation of greatness, as simply an introduction to the current state of affairs. To this end, therefore, all of the life around us is the result of thousands of millions of years of evolution. The point, however, is that we are so different from everything else, although it would be a mistake to assume that different necessarily means better. Perhaps because we are what we are, and there is no way of changing that, we tend to feel a desire to perceive ourselves as greater than we are for our own self-serving gratification.

We are bipedal, have large brains, use tools, can communicate through spoken language, appreciate literature and the

9

arts, and we have populated most of the world. Whilst these aspects of our history may collectively make us unique, how special it makes us is a matter of debate. We cannot run particularly fast, nor climb particularly well, and we cannot naturally fly at all. Our hand-eye co-ordination has suffered drastically since our evolution from the arboreal primates. Our eyesight is reasonable but not good at night, our sense of smell is of little use, and our hearing certainly cannot compete with those of many other mammals. We will not populate all the areas, nor take up as much biomass, as the whole gamut of bacteria on the planet, nor in the universe as a whole for that matter. The key to our evolutionary success has been our nature as the Jack-of-all-trades. We are not naturally exceptional at many things, whilst being naturally mediocre at just enough.

Our combination of tool use, problem solving, and teamwork has enabled us to excel in the light of our shortcomings, and persist and persevere regardless. We became efficient at what we needed for survival. That efficiency has led to technology that far surpasses the original necessity to hunt, forage and gather. It has lead to the advent of agriculture, domestication of animals, and the industrial revolution, which has ultimately led to sufficient technology to assist us in mobility and transport, in food availability, in entertainment and in medicine, and just about everything we associate with being a modern human. But what if all of these factors are so interrelated, so much a part of our now normal existence, that we find it difficult to see what we have become, or rather what it means to be a child of a modern, westernised civilisation? What if the medical profession is so overwhelmed not because of population expansion itself, but because of our current obligate use of transport, our modern foods, and our preferred means of entertainment, all of which comprise our current lifestyle? What if there was no obesity, no heart disease, negligible diabetes and negligible age-related cognitive decline? What if there were a third fewer cancer cases each year? As a society, or even better, as a global society, how difficult would this be to achieve?

Humankind:
A Natural History

Ancient Blueprints for
Contemporary People

Everything about who we are; our big brains, our upright posture, our digestive tracts, our ability to gain fat and our resilience to disease and infection are the result of how our diet has been for millions of years. In order to fully understand *why* a more archaic, natural diet might be the healthiest alternative, it is important to fully understand who we are. Or, perhaps more important still, why we are the way we are. We will then know how to change, what to change, and for what benefit we might want to change. The purpose of this section then, is purely to explore human origins in more depth, our place in nature, and some of the evidence that we have used to arrive at various hypotheses and conclusions.

Diet and The Human Genotype

"Technology... is a queer thing. It brings you great gifts with one hand, and it stabs you in the back with the other."
- C.P. Snow, New York Times, 15 March 1971

Our entire physiology has been naturally selected for over the course of millions of years, yet in the last hundred years we have become increasingly sedentary, and almost everything that we eat is farmed, even the fruits that we might expect to be entirely 'natural' and unchanged.   The result is a vast difference between our current lifestyles and that in which our genotype evolved.   The imbalance between our current existence, and that of our ancestors manifests itself in disease, obesity and ill health [16,22,40,91,144].

Our genes are those that were selected for when our ancestors were Palaeolithic hunter-gatherers.   Since then, and despite vast changes in our lifestyles, our genetics have changed very little.   Our current nutritional requirements are the result of the interaction of our ancestors with their environment, going back through time to the very beginning of life on Earth [40].

Put another way, there has not been sufficient time for natural selection to evolve an effective defence for our genes to prevent the onslaught caused by our westernised diets and westernised lifestyles [29].   Because most human diseases are so often related to lifestyle, they should be preventable.   It is the contribution of our modern stresses, our sedentary lifestyles, our consumption of farmed, manipulated and processed foods, and of chemicals, both within the foods and as pharmaceuticals, which have led to our decreasing resistance to disease [16].   To really understand what we need to be healthy, we should examine our lifestyle, including our diet, as it was when the modern human genotype was interacting naturally with its environment[40].   This, so far as can be reasonably hypothesised, was the period when mankind should be expected to be at its healthiest; physically and mentally fit, and almost (if not entirely), free from obesity and disease.

12

Researchers of human nutrition are increasingly investigating the role that our evolution has played, both in the development of our physiology and in the lifestyle-related diseases of westernised societies [134]. In the United States, for example, chronic illness and health problems either entirely or partially attributable to diet are the single greatest threat to public health. 65% of adults in the U.S. aged twenty years or over are either overweight or obese, and the estimated number of deaths due to obesity is over 280,000 per year. More than 64 million Americans have at least one type of cardiovascular disease, which represents the leading cause of mortality (38.5% of all deaths) in the United States. 50 million Americans have high blood pressure, 37 million have high-risk total cholesterol concentrations, and 11 million have type II diabetes. Furthermore, in post-menopausal women aged 50 or over, 39.6% have osteopenia and 7.2% have osteoporosis. Osteoporosis increases the risk of fractures, and osteoporotic hip fractures are associated with a 20% excess mortality in the year following the fracture. The second leading cause of death in the United States (representing approximately 25% of all deaths) is cancer. An estimated one-third of all cancer deaths are due to nutritional factors, including obesity [32]. That many of these conditions are not observed in modern populations still living a hunter-gatherer way of life, confirms the worthiness of investigations into our pre-agricultural ancestry [91,134].

The Palaeolithic

Our Hunter-Gatherer Mothers and Fathers

"The most important and urgent problems of the technology of today are no longer the satisfactions of the primary needs or archetypal wishes, but the reparation of the evils and damages by the technology of yesterday"

Dennis Gabor

The Palaeolithic began with the emergence of the Homo lineage some 2.5 million years or so ago, and the stone tools associated with our ancestors' fossils from that time. The Palaeolithic came to an end with the advent of agriculture and the start of the Neolithic, from around 10,000 years ago [96].

Up until approximately 500 generations ago, amounting to more than 99 percent of human history, all that our pre-agricultural ancestors consumed were wild meats, fish, insects, eggs, wild fruits and berries, wild vegetables and nuts, and all foraged from their natural environment [91,96,144]. Their diet contained no agricultural grains or processed foods, was low in seeds and beans, devoid of dairy foods, margarines and refined sugars, and was low in sodium. Their diet was high in fibre, lean animal protein, monounsaturated fats, polyunsaturated fats (specifically the omega-three fatty acids), and contained plenty of vitamins, minerals, phytochemicals and antioxidants [91,134,144]. Part of the reason that their diet was so healthy by comparison to ours was not simply that it consisted of an abundance of fresh meats, fruits and vegetables. The key was variety. We require about fifty *essential* nutrients for proper growth, metabolic function and cellular repair [91]. As a consequence of our dramatic change in eating habits, it should be little surprise that researchers have concluded that we are maladapted to diets of domesticated and processed plant foods [134].

14

Nowadays it would be virtually impossible to adopt precisely this type of diet again, partly because of resources, partly because of the necessities of our westernised lifestyles, and partly because we cannot know 'precisely' which foods our particular ancestors consumed out of the thousands of plant and animal species available. What is important to note, quite significantly, is that less westernised groups and modern-day hunter-gatherers are largely free from chronic degenerative diseases and biomarkers of illness (such as rising blood pressure with age, increasing body fat, and insulin resistance) [91]. Resulting from our growing awareness of this fact, a number of doctors and nutritionists are beginning to advocate a diet more closely matched to that of our Palaeolithic ancestors [91,134].

Out of Africa

A Fuller Account of Our Roots and Relationships

"No age has known so much, so many different things, about man; no age has known less than ours what man is."

Heidegger

Systematics is the system of classification that places species within various groupings, according to how closely they are related, assessed both through how the genes are expressed, such as through physical appearance, anatomy and physiology, and in the genetic relationships themselves. According to this system of classification, humans are placed within the animal kingdom, in the class of *Mammalia*, order of *Primates*, suborder of *Anthropoidea* (which includes apes, monkeys and humans), superfamily of *Hominoidea* (apes and humans), genus *Homo*, and the species *sapiens*. This classification reflects our position amongst the primates and our close relationship to the apes [112].

Our specific evolutionary lineage split off from that which led to today's chimpanzees and bonobos within the last five to seven million years [15,39,144]. Fossil evidence places the earliest members of our genus, Homo, in Africa within the last three million years, [91] with our species, *Homo sapiens*, having evolved in Africa within the last 200,000 years [144].

Evolution itself is the interaction between the genome of a species and its environment, via natural selection over time. If the environment remains constant, then the representatives of the species with the best adaptations for that environment will thrive, and their descendants will become the 'average' representatives of the species as a whole. If the environment changes, then it will be those representatives that happen to possess traits most useful for the new environment that will then thrive, and over continuing generations their descendants will become the new 'average' [32].

Where the land that a species occupies is separated, either by physical barriers such as rivers or mountain ranges, or ecological barriers such as a change in local habitat or climate, then representatives of the species in the two different areas may diversify, and 'speciation' may occur. This is to say that whilst there was originally one species, given two different environments that cause it to separate into two groups, the population in each area will develop an average that best suits that new environment. Over many generations, the offspring will become so markedly different from their common ancestor, that they are classified as an entirely different species.

Within our genome, we have some genes that are active and some that are inactive. In terms of natural selection, the genes that persist through time are the ones that, when active, contribute to the success of the individuals that have it [32,39]. Over time, therefore, the species *selects* some genes to remain in that species, whilst others may be removed by being selected against (read *The Selfish Gene* by Richard Dawkins, for a far more in-depth account of how genes interact with their environment).

When an environment changes, the individuals that were previously the best adapted for their environment, would find themselves at a discordance. The population will then tend towards the other representatives whose traits are far more beneficial in the new environment. These are the individuals that evolution will select for, and that will become the new average for future generations. At this point then, other individuals will be selected against [32,39]. If they are less in tune with their environment then they are less likely to reproduce, and because of this the less useful genes they have will effectively die out. As this happens, that discordance between the individual, their genes, and the new environment, may manifest itself through disease, dysfunction, and/or a reduced life-expectancy [39]. **This is precisely the set of circumstances that we contemporary humans find ourselves in today.** It is our numbers, modern medicine, and the lack of natural predators that will allow our species to persist, albeit with poorer health than our Palaeolithic ancestors. The diseases that do manifest themselves either do so after we reproduce, or else are not severe enough to limit our ability to reproduce, and so our species will continue to grow in number.

Encephalisation refers to the amount of brain mass an individual has, and is usually assessed in conjunction with total body mass, and can then be compared to other animals, etc. These details can be used for comparisons between genders, to assess development through life, and to compare different species and genera. Thus, a small but steady increase in encephalisation is one of a number of traits that characterises the early evolution of the primate order, between 60 and 35 million years ago. Another distinguishing feature of these early primates is that they appear to have had an increased life expectancy, relative to other mammals, and reached reproductive maturity at a later age [76]. These are also features that we can recognise within our own species, setting us apart from other mammals.

It is understood that primates evolved from the other mammals in tropical forests, approximately 65 million years ago [112]. This coincides with the extinction of the dinosaurs and the general speciation of the mammals that followed, in which new species emerged to exploit a more readily accessible environment. From 35 million years ago, the evolution of the primates branched out with the emergence of the anthropoids, which is the lineage that contains monkeys, apes and humans. A greater increase in encephalisation occurred from this point, with brain size increasing even more significantly by comparison to body size. Diet also changed, with the early anthropoids favouring plant foods as opposed to insects. Coinciding with this was a reorganisation of the sensory system, away from one based largely on olfaction (sense of smell) and hearing, and towards one almost entirely dominated by binocular colour vision. This shift in sensory bias was most likely associated with the need to recognise a diverse array of plant parts, such as fruits and leaves, as well as recognising ripeness and quality. Anthropoids tend to make their plant food choices on the basis of ripeness, fibre content, nutrients, and toxicity. The increased array of foods within the diet, which still included some animal foods in addition to the plant foods, coincided with the greater brain size and capacity to learn and remember [76].

18

The next major branch within primate evolution was to comprise the hominoidae, the branch that includes the apes and humans. According to the available molecular evidence, as measured via the immune systems of all living hominoids, we all shared a common ancestor between 15 and 12 million years ago [15]. Yet again, this branch of our distant ancestors is identified with further encephalisation. Fossil evidence points to a diet composed mainly of soft, ripe fruits. This frugivorous emphasis of the early hominoid lineage is still evident in many later species. Thus, it can be seen that we are the result of a long lineage, which from early on favoured bigger brains, longer life expectancy, and delayed reproductive maturity. Over time, our distant ancestors moved away from a diet based heavily on insects to one much more biased towards plant foods, and eventually soft, ripe fruits, in particular [76].

The word 'Hominin' refers to a bipedal species separate to the other apes. The first hominin, 'Ardipithecus ramidus', appears in the fossil record some 4.4 million years ago [113]. Disputes often erupt following new fossil discoveries, as some investigators will want to describe the bones as belonging to a new species, and others will prefer to include them within one already identified. The debate has to focus on just how different one set of bones is to another, and in the light of what we know of different but related species in the world today, whether that constitutes an entirely new species, a sub-species (close but not quite), or simply another representative of an acknowledged species. Thus, the hominin subfamily may be represented by between nine and twenty or so individual species [32,91,181]. From the earliest of these, the genus Homo began to emerge around 2.5 million years ago, the branch of which we are now the sole survivors [40].

The Homo lineage was initiated first of all with the appearance of *Homo habilis* (the handy man), associated as it was with the earliest stone tools, and *Homo ergaster*. We have evidence that since this time animal foods were holding a far more prominent place in our diets than ever before [40].

The evolution of *Homo habilis* and *Homo ergaster* took place over several hundred thousand years, during which various changes took place in the genes and behaviour of the new species [40], and

19

neither the stature nor the lifestyle of *Homo ergaster* was markedly different from our Palaeolithic *Homo sapiens* forebears, some million years later. *Homo erectus* was our first pioneer, leaving Africa and heading east into Asia. *Homo ergaster* is often confused with *Homo erectus*, and there is some contention as to whether or not they were a separate species. For the purposes of this book, *Homo ergaster* refers to a distinct species, from which *Homo erectus* probably evolved. *Homo erectus* then branched out, having some representatives going into Asia, whilst later others dispersed into Europe.

The predecessors of early Homo were the australopithecines, the youngest population of which appears to have persisted until approximately 870,000 years ago. Examples of those australopithecine fossils were found in what is now the village of Taung, South Africa [19]. The evidence from fossil sites indicates that the early australopithecines of 4-3 million years ago lived in waterside forests [174]. From the stone tool evidence, we know that *Homo ergaster* began to inhabit lakeside flood plains. As the stone tools became more diverse and specialised, as with the Acheulean technology, humans began to inhabit areas near seasonal streams [63]. The dramatic changes in diet, anatomy and behaviour that took place over the past few million years also led to distribution of labour between the sexes. There was a definite divide between the men that provided by hunting and scavenging, and the women and children that provided by gathering. This led to greater sexual dimorphism (the difference in size between males and females); greater stature in general (compared with the other apes), increased day ranges (the distances covered in search of food), increased brain size, and decreased gut size [40].

Table 1.0. Table showing where our genus, *Homo sapiens*, fits in to our family tree. This table is not exhaustive, and some investigators will give different dates and add or remove some species. Such discrepancies are due to alternative interpretations of fossil remains.

Species:	Began Appearing From:	Until:
Australopithecines	4.0 m.y. b.p.**	870,000 b.p.
Homo habilis	2.5 m.y. b.p.	1.0 m.y. b.p
Homo rudolfensis	2.4 m.y. b.p.	1.9 m.y. b.p.
*Homo ergaster**	1.9 m.y. b.p.	1.5 m.y. b.p.
Homo erectus *	1.6 m.y b.p.	50,000 b.p
Homo heidelbergensis	800,000 b.p	400,000 b.p
Homo neanderthalensis	200,000 b.p.	30,000 b.p.
Homo floresiensis	95,000 b.p.	13,000 b.p.
Homo sapiens	200,000 b.p.	Present

*There is a lack of clarity in the classifications of *Homo ergaster* and *Homo erectus*. Here, *Homo erectus* refers specifically to the fossils associated with later descendents of *H. ergaster* that emerged in Africa and then spread into Asia [192].

** Million years (m.y.) before present (b.p.)

Out of up to twenty or so species of bipedal primates that have lived since they first emerged some 7-5 million years ago, we are the only ones still alive [32,91]. Members of our species, *Homo sapiens*, have been identified from approximately 200,000 years ago, possibly up to 400,000 years ago. While there are still some slight differences between our modern selves and those more archaic *Homo sapiens* from before 200,000 years ago, it is from this time that truly modern humans (fully named *Homo sapiens sapiens*) emerged in Africa. From there, they spread across the Old World, appearing in Europe approximately 40,000 years ago [134].

21

The Environment

A Changing World and the Birth of the First Humans

Sediments taken from deep-sea cores show that from as early as 3.2-2.8 million years ago, the cycles of wet and dry climate doubled in periodicity. This change coincides with evidence from soil chemistry, pollen and various faunas, of an increase in aridity in Africa and global cooling [119,157,171,181]. Data collected from the sediments show that climate changes were occurring more frequently and were more sudden at this time [181].

The changes in climate did not have a profound effect on the environment until some time later [157]. From approximately 2.5 million years ago, the Sahara desert expanded whilst open grassland habitats spread across eastern Africa. This led to the contraction of the wooded habitats in which our distant ancestors lived [119],[157,171,181]. This drier period occurred in tandem with the expansion of the water-holding glaciers [157]. These changes were evidently reinforced by the actions of the moving continents and a long-term trend in lower levels of carbon dioxide in the atmosphere [119,157].

The closed-canopy and grassy woodlands formerly inhabited by our australopithecine ancestors began to shrink. During this time, pressure would have increased on all such populations as competition for food increased, along with the risks from predators [157]. It was during this period that the first members of our genus, including *Homo habilis*, emerged [171]. Although the australopithecines were already walking upright, the success of *Homo habilis* was due to being better able to survive in the new environment, making greater use of tools and being more efficient at moving across the opening landscape. Thus, our ancestors were already capable of moving across the ground on two legs, but selection favoured those that could capitalise on the developing species of grassland-roaming animals as a new food source [157].

Further global cooling, coinciding with another increase in aridity and seasonality in eastern Africa, occurred at a similar time to the emergence of *Homo ergaster*, between 1.9 and 1.7 million years ago [157]. Evidence for this climatic change is again found in deep-sea sediments, pollen, fossils, and so on [119]. This variable climate had a substantial effect on the diversity of mammals, which was no doubt critical in the evolution of *Homo ergaster* [171]. Furthermore, the evidence shows that the arboreal (tree-dwelling), and fruit-eating animals that were formerly common in this region, become less so at this time [119,157]. The final evidence for a global trend towards a cooler climate occurred 900,000-800,000 years ago [119].

Stable Isotope Analysis

Dietary Evidence from the Teeth and Bones

As humans, we are quite interesting lumps of carbon, hydrogen, oxygen and nitrogen. Though everything around us appears different, essentially it is just differently arranged lumps of those same chemicals. When we eat we take on yet more of those chemicals, the amounts of which depend upon how much was in whatever we were eating. The carbon and nitrogen ingested leaves a 'signature' within our bones, teeth and collagen. Carbon and nitrogen is accumulated throughout life, stopping only upon death, after which it will begin to degrade.

Molecules of carbon and nitrogen come in different isotopes, and the stable ones (i.e., isotopes that remain the same and therefore do not change into other isotopes) can be used to give a good indication of what an animal has eaten during its lifetime. Plants have particular carbon values, which are then incorporated into the tissues of the herbivores and omnivores that eat them, and this can then be transferred into the tissues of the carnivores that in turn eat them. The results of an analysis can be used to indicate which types of plants or animals, and in what ratios, a particular animal consumed during its life [101,134].

The more recent the remains from which the analysis is made, the more accurate the results are likely to be. For example, the early australopithecines consumed a particular type of carbon (on average their $\delta^{13}C$ values were most like hyenas, with a mix of C_3 and C_4 plants), but it could be from either meat sources or from underground storage organs (USOs), such as tubers and rootstocks. It might have been both. We have to combine this information with what we already know from studies of teeth, jaws and musculature, along with the habitat and the animal's digestive system, to work out the most likely reason for the values of carbon. With the australopithecines, it is quite likely that the carbon came from limited

24

amounts of meat, because it is unlikely that they could have dug into the ground to access the USOs, and then processed them accordingly, so as to effectively deal with the amount of toxins that they would have contained [112,163].

When we look at the stable isotope data from more recent remains, we can be much more precise about what the animal consumed. For example, we know that the Neanderthals (*Homo neanderthalensis*) of Western and Central Europe ate very large herbivores, such as woolly rhinoceros and especially woolly mammoth, and that these featured prominently in their diet. Smaller herbivores, such as reindeer were also consumed, but in far lower proportions [21,135]. In fact, the amount of animal protein contained in the diet matches that of carnivores [134]. This is particularly interesting, because their digestive anatomy would have been adapted for that of an omnivore. The findings of the isotope analysis also fit in with the corresponding archaeological remains found at the sites, including weapons and markings on the animal bones buried there [135].

Tooth Anatomy and Wear

The Evidence from Teeth

Wear patterns on teeth are caused by the physical consistency of food (the physical characteristics and texture), and its abrasiveness. Different teeth have different functions and deal with various types of food during the stages before the food is swallowed. Therefore, wear patterns, shape, size, and enamel thickness, can all be used to identify the foods consumed by their owner [139]. Furthermore, teeth are often the best preserved, or the only available remains of an animal. Teeth are consistently used for stable isotope analysis, the results of which can be compared with the observed features of the teeth, and what we know about the dietary habits of living descendants or close relatives [134,156].

The dentition of the australopithecines that preceded our lineage, was well suited to breaking down hard, brittle foods, including some fruits and nuts, and soft, weak foods, such as flowers, buds and aquatic herbaceous vegetation (AHV) [163,174]. Conversely, they were not well suited to breaking down tough pliant foods, such as stems, soft seedpods, and meat [163]. They could also have eaten both abrasive and non-abrasive foods, all of which suggests that the australopithecines were equally well suited to a variety of habitats, including both forests and open savannah. These adaptations allowed our early predecessors the ability to cope with short- and long-term variations in the climate and local resources, using hard, brittle foods as and when required as a fallback resource when other foods were in short supply [163,170].

Microwear analysis of the teeth of our human ancestors suggests a varied diet, albeit one that did not include significant quantities of hard or tough foods [171]. This finding is in agreement with one of the key anatomical adaptations that occurred with the evolution of our lineage, that being the increased gracilisation of the mandible and other cranial features. This change has been associated with the increased consumption of meat, and a decrease in fibrous, tough and/or brittle plant foods that require chewing or cracking [134,171]. Such foods may have been included from time to time during the course of evolution, but predominantly as fallback foods during times of limited food availability [171].

Although meat was already being consumed by the australopithecines, it may have been Homo's manner of procurement, through stone tool use, which led to larger prey being acquired and greater access to marrow and other important, nutrient-dense tissues [156]. Interestingly, the differences between the teeth of the australopithecines and our lineage vary to about the same degree as the differences between gorillas and chimpanzees. Gorillas and chimpanzees consume different diets, but there is often an overlap in fallback foods, when resources become tight. Likewise, this may well have been the case for the australopithecines and the earliest members of our genus [170].

Tool Use

Tool use was key to our success as generalised feeders. Over time, what would have begun as opportunistic and occasional hunting and scavenging, would have become an essential part of our existence. Indeed, some populations were eating as much meat as committed carnivores [181]. This was only made possible through tool use. Originally, we may simply have benefited from the use of scrapers to remove meat from bones, and then developed various tools to access brain cases and bone marrow, especially if we had to rely on the leftovers from scavenged animal carcasses. Following this, tools would have been adapted and developed for use as part of the hunt itself.

Some of the earliest stone tools, those of the crude Oldowan industry, would have allowed early humans access to brain cases and marrow from a range of animals, regardless of whether we had hunted or scavenged those animals. Chimpanzees are also known to extract brain tissue and marrow from prey animals, so it is possible that this was a dietary strategy employed for many millions of years, and our more developed use of tools simply made us more efficient at obtaining brain tissue and marrow from a greater variety of animals [40].

The reason that tools were so important was not simply to enable us to access more of a carcass than our competitors. Although we would have consumed meat all through our history as primates, the amount of meat included would have varied greatly. It was as the genus Homo was emerging, and our diets became more generalised, that meat would begin to constitute a growing proportion of the diet. Tools were required to make up for our shortcomings as primitive hunters. Unlike the big cats with their claws and blade-like dentition, we had to hunt, kill and then dismember our prey with only what we could manufacture, save the occasions when we might have been able to scavenge an animal already killed by another predator [181].

The earliest archaeological remains date to approximately 2.5 million years ago, and include both stone tools and cut-marked faunal remains from Ethiopia. This material demonstrates that the hominins of the time were making stone tools to process animal carcasses [171].

By studying what happened to the bone following the animal's death it is possible to identify which bones humans butchered after hunting [134]. Investigators examine how the animals were killed, and what would have been done to them deliberately, either by humans or other predators. Investigators would also report on what happened to the bone after that, including natural burial and abrasion by rocks, and so on.

The appearance of stone tools suggests an expanded toolkit beyond the perishable items used by living great apes for the procurement or preparation of food [171]. It is also compelling that the earliest evidence of stone tool manufacture and animal processing are found in deposits dated to approximately 2.5 million years ago, roughly coincident with the first appearance of Homo [134,181].

Over time, stone tools became more specialised, as our ancestors became better innovators. This development coincided with a greater reliance upon animals for food, particularly as our ancestors ventured out of Africa. A large number of hand axes were recovered from a site in Boxgrove, England, from approximately 500,000 years ago. These axes were associated with various large animal remains, including rhinoceroses and horses, which had been butchered by the humans living there. From 500,000-300,000 years ago, in both Hoxne and Swanscombe, England, and in Bilzingsleben, Germany, there is further evidence of humans hunting and butchering significant numbers of large animals. The evidence points towards a strongly meat-based subsistence, commencing with the first members of our genus, as demonstrated by the wealth of processed animal remains and increasingly sophisticated stone-tool technology [134].

The Big Changes that made us Human

Intestines

The ancient Greeks used to believe that illnesses stemmed from the gut [8]. The proper condition and function of our gastrointestinal (G.I.) tract is intrinsically related to, and essential for, our health and well-being. The G.I. tract represents the second largest body surface area, with the respiratory surfaces being the first. The size is comparable to that of a tennis court, being somewhere between 250 and 400 m^2. During a normal lifetime, approximately 60 tons of food passes along the digestive tract. It is because of this that the health of our digestive system is so vital, and it is therefore not surprising that it is susceptible to inflammatory diseases and cancer [16].

Most of the cells lining the G.I. tract are replaced every three or four days. In addition, the surfaces are protected by large quantities of important secretions, from saliva in the mouth to colonic secretions in the large intestine. These secretions are essential for proper lubrication and function. Furthermore, they are vital for the existence of hundreds of substances essential for the well-being of the gut's microbiology [16]. Many microorganisms in the lower intestine have strong anti-cancer properties against a variety of tumours [113]. Of the 2000 pharmaceutical drugs registered in Sweden, approximately half have reported G.I. side effects [16].

A useful line of evidence in investigating our pasts, and indeed our overall health, involves the development of our digestive system during our evolution. As with all species, the anatomy of the human gut is linked to the diet with which it has evolved. In keeping with our descent from a common ancestor, all apes and humans share the same basic digestive anatomy, including a simple acid stomach, a 'small' intestine, a small cecum with an appendix, and a markedly sacculated colon [112,113].

The most significant difference between humans and living apes is found in the proportions of the some parts of the gut. The size of the human G.I. tract, in relation to body size, is quite small in comparison to those of the apes [113]. More than half (56%) of the total human gut volume is attributed to the small intestine, whereas in apes it is the colon, accounting for 45% of the total gut volume [112].

Because the colon represents such a large proportion of the ape gut, this suggests an adaptation to a diet lower in quality than that of humans [94,112,113].

Such an adaptation amongst the apes indicates an abundance of bulky plant material, including plant fibre and woody seeds. The human gut, dominated by its small intestine, suggests a far more nutritionally dense and highly digestible diet than that of the apes [94,113]. The human gut displays adaptations that are far more similar to those of carnivores, which is a reflection of this easily digested, nutrient-rich diet [94,112]. All of the 284 species of extant carnivores have essentially the same pattern of gut anatomy, that being a simple stomach, a short gastrointestinal tract, and a colon that is not sacculated. This type of gut is incredibly simple by comparison to those of most omnivores and herbivores [112].

By comparison to gorillas and orangutans, humans and chimpanzees are far more active and social. One of the key reasons for this is diet. Gorillas are the largest living primates (Gorillas weigh up to 160 kg and 93 kg, for males and females respectively), whilst Orangutans represent the second largest non-human primates (weighing up to 69 kg and 37 kg, for males and females respectively). The problem is one of being very heavy whilst having to survive on relatively poor food. Because these two species are dependent upon lower quality plant foods, it may be the case that they do not have sufficient nutrients and energy left over following digestion, to support both adequate health and an active lifestyle [112].

Chimpanzees and bonobos, by comparison, consume a high quality diet composed of predominantly ripe fruits, supplemented with select protein-rich young leaves, and buds and flowers, as well as some animal matter, mainly in the form of invertebrates but occasionally some vertebrates, including other primates. A result of this higher quality diet is that chimpanzees and bonobos are highly active and social [112].

With regard to gut anatomy and digestive efficiency, all great apes and most monkeys can digest meat, so much so that it is often fed to chimpanzees in captivity. Within tropical forests though, such foods are often small, uncommon in significant numbers, and difficult to procure. As the tropical forests shrank, the ancestors of modern great apes moved into their own ecological niches primarily within the forests that still remained. Our ancestors, however, increased their day ranges in search of food and made a greater use of the animal food sources that were available. Meat and other animal foods provide all of the amino acids required for human protein synthesis, and animal protein is more bioavailable than the harder to digest plant proteins. Thus, a human or primate would have to eat significantly less animal protein than plant protein to derive the same benefits. Animal proteins also supply a wealth of other nutrients, such as vitamins, minerals, and essential fats, which we need for good health [112].

This shift away from the dietary strategies of non-human primates, and towards one based upon meat-eating, freed up space within the digestive tract that could then be used for the inclusion of *energy-rich* plant foods, such as fruits, nuts, roots and honey. Hence, humans began to adopt a diet based on animal foods for essential nutrients and some energy, with additional energy coming from the inclusion of high-quality plant foods. This pattern is compatible with our current gut anatomy and diet digestibility. It is even the case that many energy-rich, nutrient-poor underground storage organs (USOs), such as roots and tubers, could only be consumed because we were eating animal foods that produced detoxifying chemicals [112].

Once human ancestors had adopted their generalist diet, one that deviated significantly from that of the other apes, it then followed that the human digestive system would undergo anatomical changes. Our digestive anatomy would settle on the form and function that was the most efficient at absorbing and excreting the foods that we most commonly ate. One finding of these investigations, is that modern humans are unable to efficiently digest large quantities of uncooked vegetable matter [113]. This does not mean that vegetable foods would have been excluded from our ancestral diet, but simply that they did not constitute a large part of the diet, at least not until after we had mastered cooking.

There are in fact various differences between individuals in their gut anatomy. Hence, this discussion deals with the general comparisons between humans and apes. All living humans have a gut that is dominated by the small intestine, as opposed to the large colon that dominates the gut of living apes. These differences are the result

33

of genetic variations [112]. The contrasts between people are the result of plasticity, whereby some small changes can take place to the length of the small intestine, the colon and the size of the cecum [109,112]. The variations tend to be associated with both socio-economic status and the country of residence, rather than country of origin, so it is deemed to be a result of the environment. These adaptations within our digestive system are also related to certain illnesses that we might suffer when visiting particular regions, where differences in gut microbiology and local sanitation and hygiene may lead to travellers' diarrhoea and other signs of sickness [109]. The plasticity does not, however, deviate from the much more significant overall differences between our ape cousins and ourselves.

The reduction in the size of the G.I. tract would also have reduced its inherent energy demand. Digesting food requires energy, and the larger the gut, the greater the energy requirement. Thus, by reducing the size of the small intestine, a relative energy surplus would result. It has been hypothesised that an exchange may therefore have occurred, in which the energy-expensive gut was reduced to facilitate the growth of the energy-expensive brain [94].

Furthermore, small children would face a virtually insurmountable struggle to survive on a diet high in fibrous plant foods. Animal foods, such as meat, organs, brain tissue, viscera and marrow are highly digestible and concentrated sources of calcium, iodine, iron, sodium, and zinc, as well as vitamins A, B_1, B_6, B_{12}, niacin, folate, vitamin K, and various other micronutrients and high quality proteins [112]. Some of the fats in meat and fish products are also essential for brain growth and development.

In light of the food resources available in the changing environment, the anatomy of the early human gut, and the ability of that gut to digest certain foods better than others, it is hypothesised that the routine inclusion of animal foods was mandatory for the emergence of our lineage. Such inclusion of high-quality animal foods would have been particularly important for small children, especially with regard to their expanding large brain and high metabolic and nutritional requirements relative to adults [112].

Encephalisation

From our early predecessors, the australopithecines of four million years ago, up until the present day, brain size has tripled. This increase has not been linear, however, as there have been many variations amongst our ancestors. Encephalisation amongst the australopithecines increased from approximately 400 cm³ to 530 cm³ from 4 million to about 1.5 million years ago. The first substantial burst of encephalisation in our history occurred about 2-1.7 million years ago, coinciding with the emergence of our genus, Homo [94].

Table 2.0. Cranial capacity of humans and our ancestors

Species / Genus	Cranial Capacity	Period used for Measurements
Earliest australopithecines	400-530 cm³	4.0-1.5 million years ago
Homo habilis	600 cm³	1.9-1.6 million years ago
Homo ergaster	800-900 cm³	1.8-1.5 million years ago
Homo sapiens sapiens	1300-1400 cm³	Present

Details from Leonard *et al* (2007) [94].

The degree of encephalisation in *Homo ergaster* is actually the most impressive, as it was greater than any non-human primate alive today, and this is in spite of *Homo ergaster's* increasing body stature [94].

Whilst it might be easy to consider that larger brains are better than smaller ones, because of whatever benefits a large brain might hold over a smaller one for any particular species, any such benefits come at a cost. The brain is a vastly expensive organ, in terms of energy requirements, especially during infancy. We expend two to three times more energy on supporting our brains than any other primates [93]. For us, our hugely expensive brains could only grow due to the greater efficiency in procuring food that they conferred on us. This was not only to support our own brains as adults, but also to support the even more energy-expensive brains of infants, and for the mothers during pregnancy. It is widely regarded that the higher quality diet required for our encephalisation came from an increasing reliance on meat as a permanent, daily adaptation to our former diet strategies. It was through the consumption of meat that we were able to support larger brains, and it was partly through our larger brains that we developed cultures, technologies and more efficient foraging habits, with which we were able to out-compete our rivals and survive [93,134]. Coinciding with these changes was the decreasing reliance on more fibrous plant foods, which allowed the size of the gut to be reduced. This in turn meant that the gut used less energy and more was available for the brain [4,93].

Brain Growth from Infancy

Of all extant mammals, modern humans exhibit the largest comparative increase in brain size during infancy [157]. The brain accounts for 17% of a newborn infant's weight and 75% of the weight of the four major organs combined (brain, liver, heart and kidneys) [112]. In a 3.5 kg newborn infant, 87% of basal metabolic rate [112] and over 60% of resting metabolic rate [26], is due to the energetic demands of the brain. This figure decreases to 44% by the age of 5 years, and to 23% by the time the individual reaches adulthood. A five-year-old child has a brain approaching the energy demands of that of an adult's, but within a body that is only about a third of adult size [112].

During the first year of life, the brain grows rapidly at the time when the infant would traditionally be breastfed. The rate of brain growth then begins to slow. Historically, breastfeeding would continue, at least in part, up to and beyond four years of age. Other foods would normally be incorporated into the infant's diet from approximately six months onwards. These foods would need to be compatible with a glucose-demanding and unusually large brain, and a digestive tract that requires high-quality, nutrient-dense foods. It should not be forgotten that the brain is still only one aspect of the overall nutrient and energy requirement of a growing child, and still more high quality foods are required for growth, development, repair and activity [112].

Because of these factors it would have been a serious problem if our diet contained predominantly foods of a lower nutrient density, such as would have been the case if we ate a plant food-rich diet. Instead, it was of primary importance that growing children were weaned onto a diet containing meats, organs, viscera, bone marrow and brain tissue, which would have contained all of the necessary and essential nutrients in abundance, both for brain and general development. Conversely, a diet consisting primarily of wild plant foods would have contained far too much fibre, if it were to yield sufficient energy and essential nutrients. The human small intestine was not long enough to allow this, and as a result it would not have been adequate to support a growing human child [112].

The Neolithic

The Advent of Agriculture and the Industrial Revolution

"All of the biggest technological inventions created by man - the airplane, the automobile, the computer - says little about his intelligence, but speaks volumes about his laziness."

- Mark Kennedy

Both 'Darwinian medicine' in general, and the evolution-based nutrition that we are concerned with in particular, are based on how we lived prior to the advent of agriculture, when the Palaeolithic moved into the Neolithic, some 10,000 years ago [91]. Following a mammalian history that stretches back for tens of millions of years, the line that would eventually lead to modern humans split from the apes around six million years ago, with the first representatives of our genus living in Africa some two and a half million years ago. Since then, modern humans emerged within the last 200,000 years or so, and 10,000 years ago we marked the end of the Palaeolithic with the dawn of modern civilisation [144].

The transformation of our diet was marked at this point by the beginnings of agriculture and animal husbandry, and then, within the last hundred or so years, with industrial-scale food production and distribution technologies [144]. It is little surprise then that having limited natural selection so drastically, humankind has been able to thrive in areas all across the globe, and now numbers some six billion [91]. But, in truth, our bodies are maladapted for our modern diets and lifestyles. These cultural effects represent less than one percent of our existence as a species [144].

The sort of multi-gene mutations that would be required to prevent the chronic diseases from which we suffer in westernised civilisations, are not the sort of mutations that occur in a short period of time, such as the 10,000 years since agriculture began, nor the 100 or so years since the industrial revolution. In addition, we are not confronting one single 'disease of affluence', but many. The fact of the matter is, therefore, that while we may be enjoying life with reality TV, pizza and family cars, we are still biologically hunter-gatherers [91].

Within the medical community there is now a growing movement towards acknowledging that our modern diseases of affluence may be prevented, if we are able to compile a framework that takes into account our evolutionary past [91]. In essence, it was science and technology that facilitated our modern ways, whilst the advances in medicine in the second half of the 20th century had a global affect on health and life-expectancy [133]. It is this use of science to prolong life that needs to be taken into consideration when contemplating our position in the world. Westernised people are the only mammals to have blood pressure that increases with age, and where being overweight is becoming a norm. Modern medicine is playing a catch-up game to compensate for the pitfalls of modern technology.

When wild plants and animals were originally domesticated, their nutritional content was very much similar to that of the original wild species. Over time, those characteristics changed, slowly at first, but then rapidly following the new technologies of the Industrial Revolution. Furthermore, the advent of agriculture facilitated the incorporation of novel foods as staples of the human diet. Almost overnight cereal grains replaced fruits and vegetables as the main source of carbohydrate within our diets, a change that our genome could simply not adapt to in such a short space of time. Following the Industrial Revolution, food-processing techniques developed which confronted us with still more novel food and nutrient combinations, which again our more ancient biology had never before encountered [32].

The End of Life as we Knew It

*"The machine does not isolate man from the great problems of
nature but plunges him more deeply into them."*
- Saint-Exupéry, Wind, Sand, and Stars, 1939

The result of our 'Neolithic Revolution' was an increase in population
density, the adoption of a sedentary lifestyle, and eventually
urbanisation. Coinciding with this was a general decline in physical
health and stature, and the appearance of new nutritional disorders [134].

Agriculture itself was adopted independently in different
parts of the world at a similar time. In Asia it was predominantly rice
that was domesticated, whilst in the Americas it was maize. The
evidence suggests that both wild plants and animals were being
domesticated in the Near East approximately 10,000 years ago. It is
understood that this early farming was initiated as a subsistence
strategy to help cope with regular fluctuations in the climate [134].
Refining farming practices, leading to further domestication and
selection of wild plants and animals, took place over thousands of
years [107]. Eventually, we became dependent upon these crops and
animals, and this led to the widespread use of farming as the only
means of subsistence, for almost all of humankind the world over [134].

A key aspect of our reliance on agriculture was not just that
cereal grains were included in the diet, but that they actually became
the staples that we relied upon for survival. An example of how we
have come to understand this history can be found in Syria. The
numbers of gazelle decreased, women's bones began to show changes
related to the effects of grinding cereal grains, tools associated with
grinding plant foods were found, and then came the appearance of
domesticated sheep and goats. The evidence is further supported by
the remains of domesticated plants, and from stable isotope analysis of
diets [134]. Average stature decreased by five centimetres, due to a
combination of factors, and is understood to be predominantly due to

dietary inadequacy and some specific nutrient deficiencies. Certain childhood infections would also have had an effect [107].

It is also important to note significant changes in the teeth of individuals living in the late Palaeolithic, and those living in the Neolithic. The people of the Palaeolithic had fairly healthy teeth with no caries, whereas the increased consumption of carbohydrate-containing plant foods led to an increase in caries rates. Neolithic teeth are also more worn down and pitted, due to the inclusion of poorly ground flour. Increased caries rates are associated with the inclusion of rice into the diets of Asians, whilst a general decline in health and body stature is found coinciding with the spread of maize across the Americas. Teeth also became smaller, and rather than this being due to meat consumption, as it was in the more distant past, this time it was due to the breads and porridges which were easier to chew[134].

The adoption of agriculture initiated a trend that actually diminished the normal effects of natural selection across our species. Despite a general decrease in health, as evidenced by human remains from this point in history, the population itself began a significant expansion. Populations can only increase when food availability is greater than that which is required by the existing population. Thus, the excess provided by agriculture facilitated population expansion, even though the foods themselves were so much lower in quality that they led to poorer health. Initially, the domestication of animals and plants had only a very moderate effect on nutrient quality, but with increasing technological advances came decreasing quality. Furthermore, many of the new staples were never a part of our historical diet, and were foods with which our digestive system and our genome overall, had no experience of [32]. Our population across the world was growing and the quality of food was becoming even lower than that of the early Neolithic [134].

Following the Industrial Revolution, the advancement of food-processing technologies allowed for quantitative and qualitative food and nutrient combinations, which we had never before encountered in the millions of years of our evolution. In the United States, dairy products, cereals, refined sugars, refined vegetable oils and alcohol account for 72.1% of the total daily energy consumed.

41

These foods would have accounted for little, if any, of the energy of our pre-agricultural ancestors. Furthermore, the mixtures of some of these to make up various processed foods were also novel for our physiology to cope with, such as biscuits, cakes, breakfast cereals, baked foods and breads, crisps, chocolate, sweets and other snack foods, ready meals, pizza, soft drinks, ice cream, condiments and food dressings. All of which now dominate the U.S. diet [32] and that of other westernised populations.

Major health transitions occurred across the world in the latter half of the last century. These were facilitated by socio-economic and technological changes, which had a profound effect on life-expectancy and lifestyle. Concomitant with this have been developments in medicine and pharmacology, which have further contributed to our increased life-expectancy, and the ability to defend ourselves against diseases in the absence of more natural measures [133]. Total food production has almost tripled since the 1960s, although the world population has approximately doubled. The increased food production has been mainly in the form of greater gains from yields of cereal grains. The population is still growing though, and food provision needs to increase accordingly, potentially leading to a two-fold increase in current food production by the middle of this century. Interestingly, this surplus of food provision is not simply contributing to population expansion, it is also a key contributing factor for the worldwide increase in obesity [107].

Our more recent history is plagued by accounts of over-exploitation for the sake of easier living and easier provision of energy for survival. This has lead to species-wide extinctions on a global scale, a limitation of natural biodiversity, exhaustion of fisheries, deforestation, soil erosion, salination, chemicalisation and loss of organic material from soil, water shortages, and infections that can spread across the globe within weeks. Although climate change is in itself a natural process, the effects of our modern living will contribute to this process, affecting the state of our planet even though we are not wholly responsible. The effects may still be profound on biodiversity and agriculture. Rising sea levels will decrease coastal areas available to agriculture. Nitrogenous fertilisers increase the emission of nitrogen oxides from the soil, which results in an increase in ozone in

42

the lower atmosphere, which is an air pollutant that has adverse effects on human cardiovascular health, crops and natural ecosystems [107]. This is the world that we are now living in, where the entire human food chain is founded upon poor soil, with knock-on effects on the composition of the plant foods that grow from it, and the animals that feed upon those plants (either directly or indirectly, in the case of grain-derived foods).

In whichever regions we have tried to populate, we have destroyed forests to make way for arable land, and we have then used farming and chemical technologies that have damaged the earth. Generations later, the quality of our food has become reduced, and even potentially harmful in some cases. From the very dawn of the Neolithic, we have tried (and succeeded) to control nature to allow our species to thrive. Aside from the disastrous ecological damage this has caused, the sad truth is that we were just not perceptive and innovative enough to get the right balance between nature and self-preservation. Ultimately, many people that suffer from obesity or ill-health are simply paying the price for 500 generations of innovators who focussed on the wrong goals.

The Foundation of Modern Disease

Introduction

Perhaps the biggest scourge of westernised society is the prevalence of the metabolic syndrome, coinciding with the increase in obesity [96,107]. Throughout the world, as traditional diets become more westernised, so the frequency of Western diseases increase [112]. Cardiovascular disease, atherosclerosis, hypertension, type 2 diabetes, osteoporosis, age-related degenerative diseases, and certain types of cancer, seldom occur in our modern hunter-gatherer populations [31,133,144]. Diets of modern hunter-gatherers are far from identical to those of our Palaeolithic ancestors, but they make our best surrogate and draw many parallels. In particular, the absence of Western diseases in their populations can often be considered in comparison to the differences in nutrition and lifestyle. Such comparisons may then allow us to make projections regarding the health benefits of a more natural diet, in the prevention of chronic disease and illness [31].

Changes in dietary habits may be wholly or partially responsible for the barrage of stresses that have been placed on our bodies. These include inflammatory, infectious, ulcerative, degenerative, and neoplastic diseases. The dietary changes that may influence the onset of these various conditions could include the following: the consumption of 45 kg (100 lbs) of refined sugar per person per year, the 10-fold increase in sodium consumption; and the four-fold increase in saturated fat consumption. Fibre type, quality and quantity have changed significantly, as have the dietary proportions of some minerals, such as potassium, magnesium, calcium, and chromium [16,32]. There has been a considerable reduction in omega-three fats, membrane lipids, vitamins and antioxidants. In some severe cases, important nutrients such as arginine, glutamine, taurine, nucleic acids, vitamins, and antioxidants such as glutathione, are either not supplied in sufficient quantities in the diet [16], or are not in a sufficiently bioavailable form.

Although specific nutritional needs alter throughout life, and are affected by sex, physical activity patterns, and various other individual factors, humans generally require the same basic nutrients to remain in good health. Relatively recent changes in our diets and food choices include a reduction in diet breadth, the cooking of most foods, a heavy reliance on a single domesticated grain or crop for most of our energy needs, the selective cultivation to 'improve' our fruits and vegetables, and the consumption of highly processed foods with a concomitant increase in sugar and saturated fats. In an evolutionary sense, all of these changes occurred far too recently for our guts and digestive physiology to adapt to them [113]. It seems perhaps surprising that Darwin's theory of evolution has had such profound effects on the biological sciences, and yet is still very much in its infancy when it comes to medicine and nutrition [97].

Modern humans require a veritable suite of plant and meat foods to obtain the dozens of essential nutrients required to achieve the maximum benefits of health and longevity. The fact that this is the case for all of us suggests that this requirement evolved relatively early on in our prehistory [60].

Observational studies, whereby we observe two different populations and draw conclusions based upon their similarities and differences, cannot give definite proof of a causal relationship (in this case between disease and lifestyle). These studies do, however, lend a lot of support to the argument that adopting a lifestyle more similar to that of our Palaeolithic ancestors may prevent obesity and Western disease (even when food is available in excess) [96]. The available evidence suggests that obesity, hypertension, diabetes and cardiovascular disease are rare or unknown in populations that still have a more traditional lifestyle and dietary behaviour [97]. The increasing prevalence of chronic diseases in westernised societies, combined with our growing knowledge of the Palaeolithic lifestyle, suggests that there is great appeal in the premise that adopting the latter will help to prevent the former [31,39].

46

Metabolic Syndrome

The Metabolic Syndrome is defined as abdominal obesity plus two of the following:

- High triglyceride levels (or being on triglyceride treatment)
- Low HDL cholesterol (or on HDL treatment)
- Elevated blood pressure (or on anti-hypertensive treatment)
- Elevated fasting blood glucose levels (including having diabetes mellitus) [121]

Abdominal obesity for metabolic syndrome is defined by a waist circumference ≥100 cm (40 inches) in men and ≥88 cm (35 inches) in women. These measurements are not population specific though, so they may need to be re-evaluated for some groups to take into account differences in stature and risk [121].

Insulin resistance, resulting from the repeated release of insulin from the pancreas, leads to hyperinsulinaemia, in which insulin is chronically high in the blood as it is being continuously stimulated to remove glucose. This is the primary metabolic defect in the metabolic syndrome. This is associated with obesity, coronary heart disease, type two diabetes mellitus, hypertension, and dyslipidaemia (elevated LDL cholesterol and triacylglycerols and reduced HDL cholesterol) [32]. The metabolic syndrome may extend to other chronic illnesses and conditions that are prevalent in westernised societies, including myopia, acne, gout, polycystic ovary syndrome, epithelial cell cancers (breast, colon, prostate), male vertex balding, skin tags and acanthosis nigricans. Diseases associated with insulin resistance are either rare or absent in modern hunter-gatherers and less westernised societies, all with more traditional dietary and lifestyle habits [32].

"Human consciousness arose but a minute before midnight on the geological clock. Yet we mayflies try to bend an ancient world to our purposes, ignorant perhaps of the messages buried in its long history. Let us hope that we are still in the early morning of our April day."

- Stephen Jay Gould

Obesity

One of the most apparent consequences of our more westernised lifestyles is the unprecedented increase in obesity [59,182], which is now common across Europe and the United States [87], as well as in fast industrialising countries and urbanised areas [45,86]. The World Health Organisation (WHO) has classified obesity as an epidemic, with significant financial burdens associated with the costs of healthcare [37].

The prevalence of obesity in adults has increased by over 75% worldwide since 1980 [37]. In the U.K., prevalence increased from 6% in men and 8% in women [37,86], to 21% and 21.4% respectively, between 1980 and 2000. Approximately 55% of the adult U.K. population is either overweight or obese [37,83]. Across Europe, there are approximately 400 million adults estimated to be overweight and 130 million estimated to be obese. The prevalence of obesity has risen threefold or more in many European countries since the 1980s, mainly due to unhealthy diets and physical inactivity [183]. In the U.S. approximately 65% of adults aged twenty or older are either overweight or obese. There are 280,184 deaths in the U.S. each year ascribable to obesity. One-third of all cancer deaths are related to nutritional factors, of which obesity is just one [32].

Worldwide there are approximately twenty-two million children below the age of five that are clinically obese, and the prevalence in the U.K. rose from 1.2% in 1984 to 6% in 2002-2003 [37]. Over two-thirds of children ten years of age and older who are already obese will become obese adults. Without effective action to stem the rise, more than a million of the 8.5 million children in England will be obese by 2010 [14]. The medical concerns associated with adult obesity are mirrored in children. 25% of overweight children between the ages of six and twelve have impaired glucose tolerance, and 60% of these children have at least one risk factor for heart disease [37], such as increased blood pressure, adverse lipoprotein profiles, type two diabetes or atherosclerotic lesions [45]. 4% of all adolescents and 30% of overweight adolescents in the U.S. currently have the metabolic syndrome [37].

To be overweight is to have a body mass index (BMI) of 25 kg/m^2 or more [83,182]. Obesity is defined as a BMI of 30 kg/m^2 or more [37,83,182]. To calculate BMI, a person's weight in kilograms is divided by the square of their height in metres [45,83]. As BMI increases so does the risk of cardiovascular disease. Whilst BMI is not regarded as the most accurate method for assessing body composition, it is one of the simplest and the one that has been used in the majority of studies on health. Other methods include skin-fold thickness, hydrostatic (underwater) weighing, waist:hip ratio and electrical bio-impedance tests. None of these methods are perfectly accurate and many are costly and/or require a great deal of space and specialised equipment. It is likely that the BMI will remain the measure for assessing obesity and health risk for the foreseeable future.

The greatest increase in risk is associated with fat stored around the organs (visceral fat). Overweight and abdominal obesity are associated with increases in small, dense, atherogenic LDL cholesterol, low HDL cholesterol, raised triglyceride levels, elevated blood pressure, insulin resistance, and impaired glucose regulation including diabetes mellitus [182].

Obesity is simply the natural consequence of a long-term positive imbalance between energy intake and energy expenditure [59,83,86]. This surplus energy is then stored in the body in adipose tissue, an excess of which leads to obesity. In the U.S., only 22% of children meet the recommendations for basic physical activity levels, with 25% being classed as completely sedentary. This lack of energy expenditure, combined with the increase in energy consumption from contemporary diets, can lead to increasing weight gain and consequently to obesity [37].

Obesity significantly increases the risk of a number of diseases, including type two diabetes, hypertension, stroke, cardiovascular disease, respiratory problems, gallbladder disease, osteoarthritis, sleep apnoea, and certain cancers [37,46,83,87,183], including colon cancer [46]. These diseases may be the result of obesity on its own or in association with other conditions. Life insurance data, along with epidemiological studies, confirm that increasing degrees of overweight and obesity are important predictors of decreased life expectancy [83].

50

From a purely physiological perspective, general obesity results in alterations in total blood volume and cardiac (heart) function. Excessive fat around the rib cage and abdomen ('central' or 'abdominal' obesity [182]) restricts how far the rib cage expands, altering respiratory function. The intra-abdominal, visceral deposition of adipose tissue, associated with abdominal obesity, is a major contributor in the development of hypertension, elevated plasma insulin concentrations, insulin resistance, hyperglycaemia, and hyperlipidaemia [83].

Obesity is also strongly associated with osteoarthritis. The risk of osteoarthritis in the knee increases fourfold in obese women, and 4.8-fold in obese men, compared with those that are not overweight. The risk for knee osteoarthritis is directly linked to body mass index, and the risk increases by 15% for each additional kg/m^2 above 27. Osteoarthritis related to obesity is primarily the result of repeated and excess overloading of the joints, especially the knees and hips. Metabolic factors may also be involved, which could explain the association of obesity with osteoarthritis of the hand. In any case, it would seem prudent to reduce weight and increase physical activity, in order to help prevent or limit the progression of osteoarthritis [183].

According to the results of family, twin and adoption studies, obesity is a highly heritable condition, with an estimated 60-84% genetic contribution to BMI [37]. How genetic factors might be responsible could involve any of a number of physiological processes. Such processes could involve how often someone feels hungry, how much food is ingested before hunger is sated, how effectively the body uses the foodstuffs consumed, eating as a response to thirst, and the response to various psychological prompts to eat, such as during depression and/or for reward [37,45,83]. The precise mechanisms could therefore involve hormones, glands, receptors, adipocytes (fat cells), and all of the precursors, proteins and enzymes involved in the normal functioning of these [37]. Hence, there are a number of possibilities for genetic factors to be involved in the onset of obesity.

Although such genetic factors are of undoubted importance, the surge in obesity, predominantly in westernised populations over the last thirty years, points to behavioural and environmental changes resulting from technological advances [67,83]. In effect, while a proportion of the population may always have been more susceptible to physiological, psychological and/or emotional cues to eat more before feeling sated, or to eat more regularly, or to eat certain types of food, it has been the technological advances that have permitted these needs to be met. In other words, in the past, thanks to the types of food available and increased daily energy expenditure, it was likely that individuals with a genetic predisposition to gain weight may not have done so, because they were too active and unable to overeat.

Nowadays, with such sedentary lifestyles coupled with an excess of food availability, possibly in conjunction with psychological cues for high-energy and low-quality foods, it is clear that our environment supports our ability to gain weight [86]. So, whilst it may be easier for some people to gain weight than others, the actual principles governing weight gain and weight loss remain unchanged. In terms of effective treatment, those more biologically likely to gain weight would probably benefit more from behavioural therapies to compliment changes in their diets and physical activity levels.

Whilst there may be a number of 'quick fixes' for rapid weight loss, whether dietary, surgical or pharmaceutical, the chronic and relapsing nature of excessive weight gain and obesity raises questions as to the efficacy of any of these. The key is to find an approach that will allow for long-term maintenance of lower body fat levels, with a reduced risk of relapse to prior body weight, i.e. increasing physical activity levels and adopting a more natural diet. With such an approach, the outcome will be far wider reaching than simply an aesthetic alteration, especially as it should also minimise the risk of related chronic diseases [83]. Both obesity and metabolic syndrome are conspicuously absent from modern populations that still live a Palaeolithic/hunter-gatherer lifestyle [97].

Cardiovascular Disease

Cardiovascular disease (CVD) is a major health problem that is reaching epidemic proportions [64]. In the United States, more than 64 million Americans have at least one type of cardiovascular disease, representing the leading cause of mortality (38.5% of all deaths in the U.S.), and 50 million are hypertensive [32]. Approximately 16.6 million people die from CVD around the world each year [110]. The recent trends in Eastern Europe, including Bulgaria, Croatia, Romania, and especially the Russian Federation, from the mid-1990s, show increasing mortality from both CVD and coronary heart disease (CHD) [95].

Despite us knowing more than ever about the causes of cardiovascular disease, it is likely to worsen rather than improve over the coming twenty years [128]. As populations develop, so their exposure to the risk factors also develop. As people become older, they tend to gain weight, smoke more, become more sedentary, drink more alcohol, and eat more saturated fats [64] and salt, whilst decreasing potassium levels by consuming fewer fruits and vegetables [128]. Diet, nutrition, and physical activity levels all play critical roles in the causation of cardiovascular disease (CVD) [133].

CVD and stroke were unknown in East Africa prior to the transition to a more westernised lifestyle [96]. The low incidence of hyperlipidaemia and CVD among non-westernised populations subsisting largely on animal foods is likely to be due to a number of factors. There is now a substantial body of evidence, which shows that the total quantity of fat in the diet is less important than the type of fat, for both reducing blood lipid levels and reducing the risk for CVD. Most importantly, there are some fats that promote the risk of hyperlipidaemia and CVD, and others that lower the risk [31].

Omega-three fatty acids have a number of protective effects on the cardiovascular system, including the lowering of plasma VLDL cholesterol and triacyglycerol (TG) concentrations (n.b. cholesterol and fats are covered in greater detail in a later chapter). Provided that there are sufficient unsaturated fats, both mono- and polyunsaturated, and an appropriate ratio of omega-six to omega-three fatty acids, then it is possible to enjoy a diet relatively high in dietary fat content, whilst actually protecting the cardiovascular system from risk. The key is to limit the amount of hypercholesterolaemic fats, including saturated and *trans* fatty acids [31].

A common mistake is to believe that all fats are bad, and to then replace fats with carbohydrates. The isocaloric replacement of fats with carbohydrates often results in relative increases in plasma VLDL and LDL cholesterol concentrations and triglyceride levels, concomitantly lowering plasma HDL concentrations [31]. The evidence currently available indicates that cardiovascular health is strongly influenced by the overall diet quality, including the quantity of fruits and vegetables, and the amount of salt consumed daily. Avoidance of hydrogenated oils and fats in cooking, and the avoidance of foods manufactured using these fats, is strongly recommended, along with a regular intake of fish and the general use of cooking methods other than frying [133]. Ghee, a fat used traditionally in South Asian cooking, has been strongly related to cardiovascular disease, myocardial infarction and atherosclerosis. Production of ghee has risen sharply in Pakistan, and high levels of *trans* fats have been found within the adipose tissue of people that routinely use ghee for cooking [64].

A minimum daily intake of 400-500 grams of fruits and vegetables, including berries, green leafy vegetables and cruciferous vegetables, is recommended to reduce the risk of coronary heart disease (CHD), stroke and high blood pressure. Avoidance of sodium, whether in the form of table salt or in food additives (such as monosodium glutamate and various other preservatives), is also important for the prevention of CVD. Dietary potassium lowers blood pressure and protects against stroke and cardiac arrhythmias, and a ratio of potassium to sodium should be at least 1:1, obtained through the consumption of potassium-rich fruits and vegetables, and the avoidance of added salt [133] and salt-rich processed and tinned foods.

The high reliance of animal foods in some non-westernised populations may actually be cardio-protective. Relatively high dietary protein (19-35% of total energy) elicits a significant hypolipidaemic effect, especially in combination with a relatively low intake of carbohydrates (22-40% of total energy). Although total fat intake (of 28-58% of total energy) would be similar to, or even higher than that

54

of westernised populations, it is likely that the type of fat is again cardio-protective. The wild animal meats consumed would have relatively high levels of monounsaturated and polyunsaturated fats, with a preferential ratio of omega six to omega three fatty acids, and low levels of saturated fats. Furthermore, the diets in general would be high in antioxidants, vitamins, minerals, and phytochemicals, and low in salt. These dietary factors would be combined with high levels of physical activity, less psychological stress, and no smoking, so as to further deter the development of CVD [31].

A sedentary lifestyle is associated with an increased risk of CVD. Conversely, physical activity is associated with a reduced risk, with the level of lowered risk being related to the intensity of the exercise. Importantly, physical activity also reduces the risk of CVD indirectly, by facilitating weight loss in overweight individuals (or preventing weight gain), by preventing or delaying the development of high blood pressure, by increasing HDL cholesterol concentrations, and by lowering the risk of developing diabetes mellitus [182].

Coronary Heart Disease

In 2002, coronary heart disease (CHD) was the cause of 7.2 million deaths worldwide [110], and is the leading cause of death in both men and women in most industrialised countries [79]. CHD is the most common cause of premature death in the U.K., with one in four men and one in six women dying from it each year. CHD caused 125,000 deaths in the U.K. in 2000 and there are approximately 274,000 myocardial infarctions each year. CHD costs the UK's National Health Service (NHS) approximately £1.6 billion each year, and yet only one percent of that is spent on primary prevention. In total, CHD costs the U.K. economy approximately £10 billion each year [128].

Observational studies in both men and women have found that CHD risk is lower in those whose diets are lower in saturated fats, and higher in fruits and vegetables, in addition to those with increased levels of physical activity [79]. A reduction in blood pressure, either through diet or physical activity, by an average of 12/6 mmHg can reduce strokes by 40% and CHD by 20%. A 10% reduction in plasma cholesterol has been shown to reduce the incidence of CHD by 25% over five years. There is no age for which the benefits of these CHD-lowering steps have not been shown [182]. Someone with low LDL cholesterol levels will almost certainly not have a myocardial infarction [128].

Modifiable risk factors for CHD include:
High LDL cholesterol
Low HDL cholesterol
High blood pressure
Smoking
Lack of exercise
Diabetes and glucose intolerance
Central obesity
Oral contraceptives [128]

Protective factors against CHD include exercise, dietary monounsaturated fat intake, fruit and vegetable intake, high HDL cholesterol, and fish consumption [128].

Coronary Artery Disease

Coronary Artery Disease (CAD) occurs as a result of the arterial lumen narrowing. Its clinical manifestations include angina and myocardial infarction. Cardiovascular events, such as myocardial infarction, account for 75% of the observed mortality in individuals with existing coronary disease [41].

The major lipid alterations associated with the progression of CAD include increases in total and LDL cholesterol, and triglyceride levels, and decreases in HDL cholesterol. Further, the composition of LDL and HDL cholesterol also changes. One of the key factors in limiting the progression of coronary artery disease (CAD) is the treatment of plasma lipids [41]. Increasing aerobic exercise, whilst maintaining an ideal body weight and cessation of smoking, are all linked with the lowering of LDL cholesterol and triglycerides, and increasing HDL cholesterol [41,182]. Furthermore, reducing saturated fat intake may, in some cases, reduce plasma LDL levels by 5-20% [41]. Conversely, as consumption of saturated fats increases, LDL cholesterol levels increase too [182]. *Trans* fats have an LDL-raising and HDL-reducing effect. Mono- and polyunsaturated fats (of the naturally occurring *cis* form) reduce total and LDL cholesterol. Plant sterols (phytosterols) and stanols inhibit the absorption of cholesterol from the gut. Sterol products may reduce LDL levels by up to 10-15% [41,182], and are now being included in some margarines and other foods, along with the related marketing. Consumption of omega-three fatty acids has also been shown to reduce coronary mortality [182].

Atherosclerosis

Atherosclerosis is now a typical part of the aging process in Western societies, yet it does not affect other free-living mammals with their natural diets. Animal experiments have shown that the promotion and regression of atherosclerosis is highly responsive to dietary manipulation, far more than either psychological stress, physical inactivity or smoking alone [97].

Studies have found that meat may be less atherogenic than soy beans, low fat milk, and high fat milk. There is also some evidence that cereals may promote atherosclerosis. Wheat consumption is related to the atherosclerotic process through a number of mechanisms. The lectin in wheat increases the permeability of the intestines, enters the circulation, and activates platelets and certain cell adhesion molecules, thereby affecting the artery walls and insulin activation. In addition, cereals are low in vitamins C, D, B_{12}, folic acid, biotin, potassium, selenium, zinc, flavonoids, carotenoids, taurine and omega-three fatty acids. The bioavailability of vitamin B_6 and magnesium is also low. Each of these nutrients has been suggested to prevent atherosclerosis [97].

The increase in blood pressure that we associate with age is exclusively an issue for people in western cultures. No other mammals experience this increase in blood pressure with age. Likewise, amongst human populations living a more traditional lifestyle, such as modern hunter-gatherers, subsistence horticulturalists and traditional nomads, there is little or no age-related increase in blood pressure [97].

Cancer

Cancer is a major and growing clinical problem in modern societies [131]. In the United States, cancer represents the second leading cause of death (25% of all deaths), and an estimated one-third of all cancer deaths are due to nutritional factors, including obesity [32,78]. Although cancer is often considered to be a single disease, the name actually refers to more than two hundred different pathologies, all characterised by an uncontrolled cell growth, followed by the invasion of surrounding tissues and then metastasis to the organs of the body [131].

Many cancers primarily occur later in life, often following the optimal age for reproduction. From an evolutionary perspective, if a life-threatening condition occurs after the individual has reproduced, there will not be strong selective pressures to adapt and prevent such conditions. Furthermore, such life-threatening conditions, when they are associated with our diet and nutrition, face a massive imbalance between technological advances leading to change, and the slow deliberate pace of evolutionary adaptation and biological defence. In short, we were never biologically selected to eat the way that we do, and we have not evolved with a natural ability to defend ourselves against such an onslaught. The effect of this includes the manifestation of various cancers [29].

Since the 1970s it has been noted that westernised countries have high rates of cancers of the colorectum, breast and prostate. Overall, lung cancer is the most common cancer in the world, and the most common cancer amongst men, whereas in women it is cancer of the breast. The prevalence of breast cancer is five times greater in westernised countries than in developing countries, and obese postmenopausal women are at the greatest risk [78]. Prostate cancer is virtually absent in aging animals in captivity, which do not share a westernised human diet. Approximately 90% of prostate and breast cancers are sporadic and acquired, with only about 10% being inherited. The prevalence of other cancers may also be related to our contemporary diets. The incidence of stomach cancer is very high in Japan, but when Japanese people move to the United States, the risk of incidence dramatically decreases in those individuals [29], thus demonstrating that stomach cancer is something that the Japanese are particularly exposed to in Japan, rather than any genetic factors.

The incidence of oesophageal adenocarcinoma is the highest in Great Britain, followed by Australia, the Netherlands, and the United States. Amongst the white male population of the United States, the incidence of this type of cancer has been increasing by almost ten percent a year, which exceeds that of any other type of malignancy in that population. Although oesophageal adenocarcinoma is still relatively rare, with improving survival rates, it is still a highly lethal cancer, with a five-year survival rate of only about ten percent in Western populations [87].

A high body mass index has been associated with an increased risk of oesophageal adenocarcinoma, and with obesity on the increase in westernised populations it stands to reason that the incidence of this cancer will also rise. Whilst it is clear that much more research needs to be done in this area, and particularly with regards to the identification of dietary risk factors, it is currently accepted that a low fruit and vegetable intake, along with a low fibre intake, seem to represent the greatest dietary risks [87].

The increasing global incidence of pancreatic cancer has also been associated with the side-effects of our more affluent lifestyles. In 2000 there were 217,000 new cases of pancreatic cancer and 213,000 deaths worldwide. In Europe there were 60,139 new cases (representing 10.4% of all digestive tract cancers) and 64,801 deaths. The late presentation of pancreatic cancer, combined with the aggressive nature of this disease, mean that only a mere 10-15% of patients can undergo potentially corrective surgery. Without treatment, metastatic pancreatic cancer has a median survival of three to five months and six to ten months for locally advanced disease, increasing to approximately eleven to fifteen months following resectional surgery. Age, smoking, new onset of diabetes mellitus, increasing BMI, chronic pancreatitis, hereditary pancreatitis, and an inherited predisposition to pancreatic cancer are all key risk factors. Dietary factors associated with an increased risk include the consumption of processed and red meat, and a reduced intake of folate and methionine [50]. Precisely how red meat is a risk factor is not clear,

61

but it could be due to novel chemical or biological agents in the meat, a high saturated fat content, the level of processing, or simply the quantity of meat combined with an inadequate quantity and variety of other important foods.

Colorectal cancer (CRC) is the second most common cause of cancer death in Britain [46,72]. It is one of the most common cancers in the developed world [36,129,161]. Colorectal cancer survival rates are poor, with an overall five-year survival rate of approximately 45% [36]. Recommendations to decrease the risk of death from colon cancer include weight loss if overweight and exercise [46].

The causes of CRC could include environmental, dietary and genetic factors [36,129]. High vegetable consumption and fibre intake are associated with a reduced risk [56,98,129], whilst high energy intake, refined sugar, and some types of red meat are associated with an increased risk [155]. The consumption of certain types of red meat that leads to an increased risk may possibly be due to the formation of chemical carcinogens in the gut [56,129]. The links between vegetable and fibre content versus meat protein and fat in the diet should really be viewed together. Processed and preserved meats contain compounds that may directly increase the risk of cancer. Furthermore, cooking meat can produce some potentially harmful by-products in the gut [56]. Specifically, red meat causes the production of sulphur, which is where these links may have arisen. The risks are reduced if red meat consumption is combined with a high fruit and vegetable intake.

Sulphur and sulphate may both cause damage to the colon. The major dietary sources of sulphur are red meat, cheese, milk, fish, nuts and eggs. Sulphate is contained within brassica vegetables and preservatives within processed foods, particularly breads, beers, sausages, and dried fruit [73]. Further investigation is required before strong conclusions can be drawn, but it makes sense to limit the foods with the least nutritional benefit, such as dairy products, processed foods, breads, beer, sausages and dried fruit, whilst reducing consumption of red meats and increasing consumption of fruits and green leafy vegetables. Some, but not all, organic products are free from added sulphates. The highest risks overall are likely to be associated with high intakes of processed meat and fat with

62

insufficient vegetable and fibre intake [56,129]. The effects of different nutrients on the colonic microflora may also be intrinsically involved in the prevention of cancers. Although the evidence is not conclusive, colonic flora may be a major environmental factor that modulates the risk of colorectal cancer in humans [56].

Interestingly, other studies found that all macronutrients (proteins, fats and carbohydrates) were significantly associated with survival, with the strongest effect being for fats. It is important to note that some research assesses cancer prevention, whilst other research assesses survival rates (essentially prevention versus cure). For example, a high calorie intake is associated with an increased risk of colorectal cancer, but it is also associated with increased survival. Specifically though, the findings actually point to polyunsaturated fats being the key to increased survival rates, rather than overall energy intake alone [36].

The liver is the main organ responsible for the detoxification of numerous substances, including carcinogens. As such, cirrhosis (whereby the liver is damaged sufficiently to cause fibrous scar tissue to develop) has been linked to an increased risk of cancers in the respiratory and gastrointestinal tracts, as well as the urinary organs [34]. Cirrhosis is most commonly associated with excessive alcohol consumption, but some drugs and chemicals can also lead to the condition. Various drugs and chemicals (including pharmaceuticals), can lead to some level of liver damage in any case, but not necessarily cirrhosis.

Diet is considered to be a contributory factor to the onset or progression of a number of cancers. Epidemiological studies indicate that diet composition may be related to 35% of cancer deaths in humans [106]. It is also important to understand the effects of dietary factors on hormone levels, and in turn to understand the effects of hormone levels on cancer development. Oestrogens are made in the body primarily from testosterone, and the ratio of oestrogens to androgens can be altered by body mass and the percentage of fat within the body. Over-exposure to oestrogens has been implicated as a high risk factor for breast cancer, and they have a wide variety of biological effects on the prostate too. In addition, the effects of phytoestrogens, which appear in some food sources, have the ability to perturb our hormone balance [29].

The association between certain foods and cancer has been reinforced throughout the scientific literature. Salt-preserved or smoked fish and meats, cured meats, foods processed by direct fire drying, and the consumption of pickled foods, including pickled vegetables, have all been associated with an increased risk of a number of cancers, including colorectal cancer [68,82], lung cancer [175], respiratory tract cancers (specifically nasopharyngeal carcinoma) [177], and gastric cancer [77,78,137,167]. With regard to the latter, diets containing low levels of fruits and vegetables increase the risk of gastric cancer the most [5].

Cooking meat is also associated with increased formation of carcinogens [164]. In particular, the smoke produced from broiling fish increases the prevalence of factors associated with cancer development. Charred parts of broiled fish, as well as medium or well-done beefsteaks, hamburgers and beef extract have all been found to contain carcinogens [116]. In addition to the increased risk from charred meat, it is cooking meat at high temperatures that also leads to the formation of harmful chemicals [78].

Sources of the carcinogens associated with colorectal cancer include smoked fish, salted fish, beer, cured meats and sausages, but not other meat products. In some cases the association is weak, but nevertheless present. Although beer contains the same chemicals, it has not actually been found to be associated with colorectal cancer risk, possibly due to developments in the methods of drying malt. Similarly, the levels of carcinogens in cured meats have also been reduced, primarily due to changes in processing methods [82]. Importantly, the carcinogenic chemicals are only activated through specific changes that occur during processing and preparation, such as preservation and high temperature cooking, and are not found in fresh meat. Similarly, carcinogenic effects of fresh poultry have not been found [78].

Restricting salt intake, whether through avoiding salted foods or by not adding salt to food at the table, has been found to reduce the risk of gastric cancer [167]. Sound advice is to avoid overcooking meat or the juices, and to avoid charring the surface of meat and fish.

Preferably, meat and fish should be wrapped in aluminium foil for cooking, and any charred food should not be eaten. Meat should be cooked without coming into contact with naked flames, preferably at a low temperature, with the avoidance of overheating [30,116].

Importantly, the consumption of green vegetables has been found to lessen the load of some of the carcinogens formed in cooking, both through the protective effects of some of the nutrients, and because chlorophyll can bind the harmful chemicals and enhance their excretion in faeces [116]. Furthermore, a diet high in nitrates does not appear to confer an increased risk of gastric cancer, provided that diet also happens to be high in a variety of fruits and vegetables [77]. The available evidence suggests that we should favour fish, poultry, meat from non-domesticated animals and waterfowl in place of red meat. Red meat should typically provide no more than 10% of total energy intake [30].

Folate is inextricably linked with DNA synthesis and replication, and deficiencies of this vitamin have consequently been associated with an increased risk of some cancers [51,80]. Epidemiological studies have suggested a link between insufficient folate levels and the risk of cancer of the colorectum, oropharynx, oesophagus, stomach, pancreas, lungs, cervix, ovary, and breast, as well as neuroblastoma and leukaemia. Several large prospective studies suggest a 40% reduction in the risk of colorectal cancer and adenomas in individuals with the highest intake of folate, compared with those with the lowest intake. Because of various serious side-effects associated with folate supplementation [80], it may be appropriate to seek a natural and complete source of dietary folate [51,98], rather than to rely on supplements. Such considerations should be taken into account on an individual basis with a G.P. or other suitably qualified medical professional. Good sources of folate include liver and green leafy vegetables.

The effective medical treatment of cancers, including various combinations of surgical resection, radiation and/or chemotherapy, depend upon the detection of cancer at a very early stage. Unfortunately, it is often not possible to identify and screen all individuals at risk, and patients often present to their G.P. when the cancer is already in an advanced stage. Consequently, it is generally

65

agreed that the most effective means of controlling cancer within society is to find effective means of preventing it [176].

It is the natural state of the body to replace old or damaged cells with new ones, and in some areas cells are replaced every few days. Cancers can result when faults occur in this process, suggesting that the issue could involve the replication blueprint (DNA) or the building blocks of the new tissue, including proteins, lipids and other nutrients. Dietary factors, either to supply sufficient building blocks and other essential nutrients, or to prevent damage to DNA, are therefore likely to play a key role in the prevention of cancer. Similarly, limiting damage by reducing exposure to harmful substances, such as those from smoking or certain chemicals added to foods, may be of equal or even greater importance. Cancers are the result of natural processes that have gone wrong, and preventative steps will never be enough to avert all possible cancers developing, but such steps might be effective in at least reducing the risk, limiting the development and/or aiding recovery. With more than 30% of all cases of cancer being preventable by feasible dietary measures, physical activity, and maintenance of appropriate body weight, between three and four million cases of cancer could be prevented worldwide every year [30].

Type II Diabetes Mellitus

Diabetes Mellitus (DM) is a disease characterised by a chronically elevated blood glucose concentration. There are two types of diabetes, described as either type one or type two. Former descriptions, such as juvenile-onset and adult-onset diabetes mellitus, have had to be abandoned. Type two, formerly adult-onset, used to occur primarily in adults over the age of forty. We now have the condition occurring in children younger than five years of age. Eleven million Americans currently suffer from type two diabetes [32].

Whereas type one diabetes may result from the body producing the wrong type of insulin, or following an infection or severe stress, type two diabetes is most often the result of diet and lifestyle factors. Type two diabetics are generally insulin-resistant, that is, the insulin that they produce is inadequate to remove sufficient glucose from the blood. This may be because of too much body fat, and/or because of a diet that contains too much high-glycaemic-load carbohydrate, which would be constantly driving blood glucose levels up.

The goal in the prevention, management and treatment of type two diabetes mellitus is an improvement in insulin sensitivity, which can be achieved through modifying the diet and increasing physical activity, especially through resistance training. Low to moderate glycaemic load foods should account for dietary carbohydrate intake. Some animal studies suggest that protein quality may be an important factor in the onset of type two diabetes [97].

The apparent absence of diabetes amongst many traditional populations is understood to be primarily due to their lack of abdominal obesity and insulin resistance. As with increasing blood pressure, the decreasing insulin sensitivity associated with age in westernised population, should not be regarded as normal biology. Studies have shown that populations living a traditional lifestyle are significantly more insulin sensitive, compared with people of a similar age from westernised populations [97].

The consequences of insulin resistance may only begin with the metabolic syndrome and cardiovascular disease. The chronically

67

elevated insulin levels in the blood (hyperinsulinaemia) has a profound effect on endocrine pathways and may facilitate the growth of various tissues, the consequences of which could include polycystic ovary syndrome, acne vulgaris, epithelial cell cancers, and myopia, as well as the trends towards increased stature and earlier puberty [97].

Interestingly, the body has begun to protect itself against some of this damage, although this is limited in effect, with people of European descent being slightly less prone to diabetes and insulin resistance than people from other regions of the world [97]. Control of type two diabetes can be achieved through dietary modifications, weight loss if overweight, and increased physical activity. The prevention of cardiovascular disease should be an integral part of the management of diabetes, in addition to the management of diabetic complications, such as neurology, nephropathy, retinopathy, and proteinuria [182].

Inflammatory Bowel Disease

The rising incidence of inflammatory bowel disease (IBD) over recent decades also coincides with profound changes in dietary and lifestyle patterns. A high intake of red meat, processed meat and alcohol has been positively associated with IBD, whilst fruit consumption is inversely related to its development. Intestinal sulphur has been associated with damage to the mucus lining of the colon, as well as other protective functions of the lower intestine. As discussed previously, sulphur is created exogenously from various foods, including red meat, cheese, milk, fish, nuts, and eggs, or from the preservatives within other foods, such as breads, beers, various other alcoholic drinks, sausages and dried fruits [165].

Of this list, fish is the only one to feature that still exists in a similar manner to the fish that our ancestors would have eaten. Red meat has been changed through livestock domestication, and eggs and nuts would have constituted a very small component of our ancestor's diet. It is not simply the foods themselves, but the entire lifestyle as well, in addition to specific dietary countermeasures. Gut health would be vastly improved if we were consuming the amount of plant food that our ancestors did. Various other improvements to gut health would have resulted from greater levels of daily physical activity and a more favourable gut flora. If this were achieved, then the consumption of high amounts of wild fish, moderate amounts of red meat, and the inclusion of lesser quantities of eggs and nuts would be far less likely to encourage IBD than some of those foods do now.

Oxidative stress is also understood to be involved in the development and progression of IBD. This is because inflammation along the intestine is associated with the increased production of free radicals. Whilst anaemia is a common problem amongst women, caused by blood loss during menstruation, men are most likely to suffer from anaemia only if they are losing blood through the intestine, possibly as the result of IBD. Iron supplementation is a common recommendation in the treatment of anaemia, but it has been associated with a decrease in antioxidant vitamins and can increase sulphur in the intestines and further support the progression of IBD [164].

The resident bacteria of the gut are suggested to be an essential factor in the inflammatory processes associated with IBD [56]. Specifically, the resident bacteria can influence which other bacteria may be present in the gut, and which may be restrained or suppressed. By not allowing proper colonisation of the gut from birth, and by not nurturing proper bacterial presence through life, it may not be possible for sufficient numbers of good bacteria to proliferate effectively, or else for there to be unfavourable ratios of them to potentially more harmful bacteria. Studies have shown that plant foods that are high in certain types of fibre increase the populations of *Bifidobacillus* and *Lactobacillus* in the colon. These bacteria, in turn, affect local metabolism and may have a protective effect against IBD [165]. Correcting gut flora through the use of antibiotics is proving less useful, following the increases in antibiotic-resistant strains. Hence, research into antibiotics has been superseded by research into the use of probiotics, with the aim of nurturing a positive balance of healthy bacteria [56], and hopefully a healthier gut as a result.

Osteoporosis

In post-menopausal women aged fifty years or older in the United States, over 7.2% have osteoporosis and 39.6% have osteopenia. Osteoporotic hip fractures are associated with a 20% mortality rate in the year following fracture [32].

The commonly associated risk factors for osteoporosis are physical inactivity, weight loss, low calcium intake, vitamin D deficiency, smoking, and alcohol consumption. A common reaction to this is often to do some exercise, take calcium and vitamin D supplements, and to cut down on smoking, if applicable. As a more natural, and hopefully more agreeable alternative, the Palaeolithic lifestyle included significant amounts of outdoor walking, high calcium bioavailability due to a low intake of beans and cereals, and low urinary losses of calcium because the intake of sodium was so low. The intake of highly bioavailable calcium would have come from the high intake of certain plant foods, such as green leafy vegetables. These are also high in potassium, which has an alkalinising effect that helps to prevent urinary calcium loss [97].

There has been some dispute regarding optimal protein intake. These arguments are based on the effects of protein on net acid load. In this regard, acidity is promoted by the ingestion of meats, cheese, cereals, beans and added salt. Although meat is net acid-producing, the effects would have been ameliorated when it constituted part of our ancestral diet. A balanced, natural diet high in meat, fruits and vegetables is preferable for maintaining the body at close to its optimal pH of 7.4. It is the combined effect of cereals, beans, cheese, and salt, with the associated insufficiency of fruits and vegetables, which leads to an acid-producing environment, and these acid-producers are predominantly modern foods. Calcium is then released from the bones to help maintain the alkaline pH of 7.4. Consequently, consuming foods that promote an acid environment encourage calcium loss from bones, which in turn increases the risk of osteoporosis. Most studies that compare vegetarians with omnivores, suggest that bone mass is the lower in vegetarians. Furthermore, people with diabetes and/or insulin resistance may have brittle bones, despite an increased bone volume [97].

Ageing

Up to 62% of institutionalised older people suffer with dementia. One study found that under-nutrition was reported in 45.5% of people in long-term care [122], and another that patients aged seventy-five years or older had poorer nutritional status than those younger than seventy-five years [43]. Physical, psychological, social and cultural factors may all have a negative effect on dietary intake and metabolism [122]. Alterations in the senses of taste and smell, and poor dental health, all directly decrease food intake and/or influence food selection [43]. Furthermore, the increasing use of medication by older people, in addition to gastrointestinal changes affecting the bacterial ecosystem, can have a negative impact on nutrient absorption [122]. A lower food intake leads to the reduced consumption of both macronutrients and micronutrients, and mild, sub-clinical deficiencies are known to be common even in otherwise relatively healthy persons [43].

Mental decline may be accelerated by insufficient macronutrient consumption, compounded by a potentially increased micronutrient requirement. Whilst inadequate nutrition may not be the primary cause of dementia and mental decline, it is at least likely to be a significant contributing factor. It remains to be determined whether it is cognitive decline that leads to poor nutritional status, or the poor nutritional status that affects cognitive decline [122]. It is also not clear as to whether the apparent nutritional deficiencies in older individuals are due to insufficient nutrient intakes, an increased physiological demand for nutrients, or simply reflective of other underlying health problems [43]. What has been shown, however, is that diet affects memory and learning, which is suggestive of the brain's vulnerability to an inadequate diet [122].

Alzheimer's disease (AD) is an age-associated neurodegenerative disease, which affects up to 50% of people in the US, between seventy-five and eighty-four years of age. AD is characterised by a progressive memory and language impairment, often accompanied by behavioural symptoms, including anxiety and depression. Both animal and human studies have found links between the consumption of cholesterol and saturated fats, and Alzheimer's disease. Additionally, high carbohydrate diets, which are a relatively new dietary behaviour, influence lipid metabolism and may play an important role in the development of AD [172]. The brain requires specific fats for health, and imbalances between saturated and unsaturated fats, combined with potentially inhibiting effects of high carbohydrate diets on lipid metabolism, may be key influences in the onset and progression of Alzheimer's disease.

With regard to the micronutrients, a deficiency of vitamin B_{12} is estimated to affect 10-15% of people over the age of sixty. Niacin status is also noticeably low in this population, which raises concerns due to niacin's protective effects against cancer development. The evidence from scientific studies suggests that increasing physical activity, along with increasing consumption of dietary niacin [122], folic acid, vitamin B_6 and vitamin B_{12}, may all have beneficial effects on cognitive function and well-being in older people [173]. Research suggests that reducing blood pressure may also reduce cognitive impairment in the older population [182].

Contemporary Versus Palaeolithic Diets

Foraging

The diet of chimpanzees is primarily made up of ripe fruit, with other plant products constituting an important secondary food source. It also includes some animal foods, such as termites, ants, eggs, and occasionally small mammals [112] and birds [76,125]. More recent observations have detailed how chimpanzees hunt and eat monkeys and even other chimps. However, the greatest proportion of the diet of extant apes and monkeys is from plant foods (new leaves, ripe fruits, seeds, exudates, nectars, flowers, pith), with only trace to moderate amounts of animal matter, usually in the form of invertebrates. Importantly, because such a variety of different plant foods are eaten together, along with their varying nutrient constituents, there are doubtless positive health implications that are as yet poorly understood [113].

Two key changes that took place when our first human ancestors moved away from the apes, were in how they foraged for food, and what they ate. Analysis of microwear patterns on teeth, along with analysis of stable isotopes of tooth enamel, offers valuable evidence that the australopithecines consumed a variable diet of both plant and animal foods. The plant foods would have included fruits, seeds, grasses and tubers, whilst animal foods would have included invertebrates, insects, and possibly some scavenged or hunted meats [94]. It is important to keep in mind that just because the common ancestors of ourselves and chimpanzees lived several million years ago, they were still exceptionally well adapted to their environments, otherwise they would have become extinct there and then. In addition, because we know our more recent ancestors hunted meat, and because chimpanzees do hunt meat on occasion, it is not unreasonable to suppose that our common ancestor behaved likewise.

Thus, it was 1.8 million years ago, coinciding with both the emergence of *Homo ergaster* and significant changes in the climate, that the foraging and dietary behaviour of our ancestors changed [94]. The long-term changes in climate would have affected the whole environment and landscapes, causing our ancestors to adapt their dietary strategies to exist more efficiently in their new surroundings.

A consequence of this may have been the division of labour between male and female, the young and the old. In keeping with what we know about modern hunter-gatherers, as well as chimpanzees, it is the males that form the hunting parties. In hunter-gatherers, this leaves the females and the young to remain at or in the vicinity of the home base. Thus, from approximately 1.8 million years ago until very recently, the males would have spent their days hunting, whilst the females, the children and the elderly participated in food gathering and preparation. Rootstocks, for example, require an element of digging, and must often be crushed, soaked and cooked to remove toxins and improve nutritional content [132]. This is therefore something that is associated with the non-hunting members of such groups.

As many foods would have been gathered from the area surrounding the home base, it is likely that the females and juveniles would have gone out gathering, whilst the older people would have cared for the infants and remained at home to prepare the food. This is a fair hypothesis for the emergence of child-care within extended families and larger groups. This meant that all adults and juveniles fit enough were able to contribute directly to the amount of food brought into the home base, which would have then been shared around. Thus, the provision of child-care by the elders would have had an indirect positive effect on the amount of food gathered, as the mothers were not bound to remain at home to look after their infants. This, in turn, would have contributed to the success of the local population as a whole.

Underground storage organs (USOs) include bulbs, corms, rhizomes, taproots, tubers and rootstocks. They contain both water and carbohydrates [171]. Because they would have been available to our ancestors, it is often thought that they would have been included in the diet. There is even some evidence from tools and stable isotope analysis that the australopithecines may have accessed USOs. However, chimpanzees and other large non-human primates rarely exploit USOs, in contrast to many modern hunter-gatherer groups, most likely due to their inability to digest large quantities of the inherent toxic compounds [132].

Having to dig into the earth around such plants is in itself a barrier to access, and then they may be toxic anyway, and difficult to

77

digest raw. Consequently, the technology to access and prepare these would have required the development of certain tools, and the knowledge of what level of processing and preparation would be required. So, although their inclusion in the diet will have taken place during the last two million years, it is difficult to know when and to what degree [119,132,171]. The deliberate use of fire for cooking is not known until well after the emergence of *Homo ergaster*, and so the inclusion of USOs is not likely until some time after the species first emerged [7]. We do know that early humans in Africa would have had access to over 140 genera of plant foods, all of which could have been eaten without the need for cooking [125].

Finally, the requirement for early humans to travel significant distances from the home was probably not restricted to hunting parties alone. As the drier climate would have increased aridity, the distances required to gather plant foods would also have increased [119]. Thus, the changing climate meant that survival would have favoured groups where the elders managed childcare and food preparation, as the fit children and juveniles would have accompanied the females in food gathering. Simultaneously, there was an increased requirement for efficient movement across greater distances, for both the hunters and gatherers, thus facilitating our ancestors to consolidate their adaptations for bipedal locomotion. The development of more advanced tools, along with improved problem solving skills, all came together to pave the way for our success on the planet, as a result of climatic changes within the last few million years.

"In the long history of humankind (and animal kind, too) those who learned to collaborate and improvise most effectively have prevailed."

- Charles Darwin

A Natural History of Meat Eating

Meat eating itself occurs in both humans and the apes, although the sources of meat can be vastly different. If we eat meat, and our closest relatives the chimpanzees eat meat, then it is highly likely that so did our common ancestor in Africa. This would be the case even if we did not have evidence from teeth, tools, animal remains, stable isotope data, and so on. Chimpanzees consume an estimated 10 to 40 grams of meat per chimp per day, as opposed to we humans who consume between 270 to 1,400 grams per person per day. Amongst the chimpanzees, it takes many years to learn successful hunting techniques, with the older males being far more likely than the younger ones to ambush prey. Similarly, it is the older chimp males that perform the most complicated manoeuvres during the hunt, and that are best able to predict the escape routes of their prey. It is thought that the greater levels of cognitive processing required to learn these skills, are associated with the greater encephalisation of chimpanzees compared with monkeys, and hence the greater inclusion of hunting in their dietary behaviour [76].

It is the employment of hunting as a dietary strategy by humans, chimpanzees, baboons and some other anthropoids, which leads to the conclusion that hunting goes back a long time in our evolutionary past [63]. Because of the time commitment required to care and carry the young, combined with the learning period required to become an effective hunter, neither human or other primate females would find hunting profitable [76]. Hence, it is the human and chimpanzee males that are responsible for hunting [76,119]. The meat obtained is then widely shared throughout each group [119].

When the ecosystem changed between 2 and 1.8 million years ago, the number of grazing animals in the newly forming savannahs would have increased upon the East African landscape. This would have led our human ancestors, who were already eating meat, to capitalise upon and exploit these new opportunities [94,170]. Evidence is growing that early humans capitalised on the carcasses left by other carnivores, and in some cases they may have worked as a team to force carnivores away from their kills. *Homo habilis*, although only the size of the average ten-year-old, were known to have scavenged meat from the kills of sabre-toothed cats. The sabre-toothed cats had evolved such long teeth because they made them effective killers of large herbivores. In fact, the diminutive *H. habilis* would have been too small for the cats to attack, because their teeth were too big and too fragile, and their jaws too weak. The risk of breaking their teeth would have been too great, and as a consequence our ancestors were unlikely to have been hunted by them. Further, microanalysis of herbivore bone remains has revealed cut marks made by stone tools, which overlay teeth marks left from sabre-tooths. Thus, the cats made the kill, but it was human ancestors that polished off the remains.

Further evidence comes from the archaeological record of *Homo ergaster*. This is the species associated with the development of more advanced stone tools along with the first major hunting and gathering economy [94,84]. Meat eating itself most likely goes back beyond the australopithecines, at least to some degree, but with *Homo ergaster* there was a significant shift in the amount consumed. A brief examination of the dietary behaviour of extant great apes also brings us to this same conclusion, that meat eating was a key and ancient aspect of our past [7,112]. With the evolution of *Homo ergaster* approximately two million years ago, came a new reliance on meat as an integral part of the human diet [63,84].

Although some might argue that underground storage organs (USOs), such as tubers and rootstocks were being increasingly incorporated at this time, in most cases fire would have been necessary to obtain the nutrients from these foods. As controlled fire occurred much later on in human evolution, it was meat consumption that increased first, with USOs being incorporated later on, and to a lesser degree. The evidence from stone tools, the knowledge that carbohydrate-rich energy sources were not available, and the comparisons to extant great apes, all suggest how important meat eating was to our human ancestors in Africa, at least to significant degrees above that of their predecessors and non-human contemporaries [7]. Carbohydrates would have been important for contributing to energy requirements, and because carbohydrates are in any case essential for good health, they would still have been an essential part of the diet. The newly developing reliance on meat fats and proteins, however, would have supplied greater quantities and a better quality of amino acids and other essential micronutrients [112].

Animal carcasses would have been acquired through both direct hunting and from scavenging, including driving other hunters and scavengers away from carcasses. Furthermore, the bone evidence shows that some animals would have been butchered at the site of the kill, and then transported back to the home base, presumably to be shared with the other members of the group and for greater security [63,94]. Smaller animals would have been carried back whole, so the technology to butcher larger animals simply meant a greater ease of provisioning a home base. Evidence from this is found in bone refuse occurring in apparently domestic human sites dating back to almost two million years ago, and some possibly older still [63].

The development of new stone tool technologies initiated a feedback-loop with our growing brains. As the tools improved our ability to kill larger prey, and then to better access the meat, marrow and other tissues of the animals, so we became more efficient and better skilled in hunting and developing more tools [171]. New technologies of stone tools emerged, such as that of the Acheulean industry of 1.6-1.4 million years ago, which allowed humans to better process these animal and plant materials [94,134]. Evidence from this period suggests that more animal foods were available than could be consumed in one sitting. It was during this period of mass meat exploitation and cultural revolution, in which the final significant episode of encephalisation occurred, from which modern humans are the result [132].

The importance of meat in the development of the brain is twofold, both because of the increased caloric density of meat compared with plant foods, and in the type of fats then available to us in greater quantities. Again, access to the best animal fats from marrow and brain tissue required an adaptation of the early tool kit, which in turn stimulated our inventiveness and ingenuity in association with our increasing brain size [94,171]. Furthermore, the energetic costs for pregnant mothers, with larger-brained foetuses than those of our predecessors, also meant that meat eating was important in providing the necessary calories [7].

This greater reliance on meat allowed for greater year-round provision of calories and nutrition, which may then have led to shorter birth spacings, and changes in the number of dependent youngsters within the groups, cared for by the elders as well as the parents. This may have further contributed to the cultural revolution, and then the expansion of our species and its contemporaries outside of Africa [132].

As mankind left its cradle in Africa and migrated across the globe, the changing of the seasons in more northern latitudes would have had a profound effect on food resources. Plant foods would have become less abundant because of these seasonal changes, and would therefore represent a less reliable source of nutrition [76].

Our success as a species outside of Africa hinged upon our ability to use animal foods for survival. This was not just true of our own species, but for other sibling human species as well (*H. neanderthalensis*, *H. heidelbergensis*, *H. ergaster*, *H erectus*, and the most recent addition of *H. floresiensis*, as key examples). Evidence for this shift in dietary behaviour comes from archaeological sites of these humans that contained a super-abundance of animal remains along with evidence of hunting tools [76]. This increase in reliance on animal foods coincides with the absence of evidence of the use of plant foods (which is not to say that they could not have been included in the diet at all, but simply that not enough was included to leave any evidence, and no tools used in the preparation of plant foods have been found). It would be wrong to assume that the absence of evidence is the same as evidence of absence: we do not know what discoveries may yet be made. However, in this context, the super-abundance of animal remains and absolutely no indication whatsoever of plant remains, does give substantial evidence to the notion that the European humans were obtaining most, if indeed not all, of their energy and nutrition from the available animals.

Another important shift in behaviour that coincides with this is that of the family or group. In Africa, there was an efficient division of labour throughout all members of the group, but in Europe this would not have been the case for much of the year. With fewer plant resources available the women and juveniles would not have been able to gather in the same way as their African ancestors [76]. With the abundance of animals being brought back by the men, it is perhaps more likely that all the other members of the group concentrated on teaching the young, on preparing the meals, and on maintaining and developing the home environment, including provision of clothing, bone tools, and maintenance of the fire. These factors were even more important in the colder climates of the north. Women would have been able to wean their young for a longer period before the necessity to move them onto solid foods. This greater attention to their young for a longer period, may have contributed to our eventual success as a species.

A key development regarding our increased reliance on animals for survival was not just the high quantity of animal kills, but also the size of the animals [63]. A site in Boxgrove, in the South of England from 500,000 years ago, has a large number of Acheulian hand axes and remains of rhinoceroses, horses, and other faunal remains, the bones of which have clear cut marks on them. This is just one of a number of sites from this period and up to 300,000 years ago across Europe, which exhibit similar findings [60,134]. This period, the Middle Palaeolithic, was one preceding the migration of modern humans from Africa. Hence, this evidence concerns the behaviour of our contemporaries, who migrated out of Africa and across Europe before our own direct ancestors.

Ever since the emergence of our lineage in Africa, meat consumption has increased in conjunction with our increasing technology and our migration across the globe. The results of stable isotope data have shown that the protein in Late Palaeolithic humans and their contemporaries came mainly from animal sources, and of those it was most likely to have been large herbivores that made up the diet. This evidence comes from analysis of groups of modern humans and Neanderthals from between 100,000 and 13,000 years ago (analysis following 30,000 years ago would have been exclusively of our own species, as the Neanderthals were believed to have become extinct at around this time) [134]. This is a matter of common sense, in that although one large animal may be equivalent to the combined weight of many small animals, it is far more energy-efficient to make only one kill. Additionally, larger species generally have a greater percentage of body fat, and so their total energy yield on a weight-by-weight basis would be greater [31].

Studies of the Europeans during the Palaeolithic show that their diet was indistinguishable from those of top-level carnivores, such as arctic foxes and wolves. As humans, we have a limited ability to synthesise taurine from other amino acids. By adopting a diet high in animal proteins (which would have included taurine), there would have been no selective pressures for us to synthesise the amino acid from plant foods [31].

One of the key differences between the protein sources for Neanderthals, and for modern humans of the last 30,000-20,000 years, is that our protein came from a more varied range of foods than for the Neanderthals. Specifically, we were incorporating aquatic foods in our diet [134]. This is particularly important when we consider that Neanderthals, along with all of our other contemporaries, were extinct by around 30,000 years ago. Whether or not this was down to food choices and dietary initiative on our part, or pure territoriality against the Neanderthals which prevented them from accessing waterfronts, is not currently known.

Interestingly, this dietary shift towards aquatic resources became far more extreme much later on (around 10,000-5,000 years ago, depending on the area). Evidence of freshwater fish consumption, such as from isotope studies of humans living in the Danube gorges of South-eastern Europe, is supported by the archaeological evidence of fishing equipment and large numbers of fish bones. Further, in coastal regions of Denmark and England, isotope evidence suggests that marine fish were the primary source of protein [134].

During the Middle and Late Pleistocene, the range of humans extended into cold-temperature and sub-Arctic regions. This would have almost certainly led to the diet of such populations being almost exclusively meat-based [63]. This is important to bear in mind as many pregnant women feel an aversion to meat. Whether or not this is a modern phenomenon, associated with the poorer quality of meat available as a result of high-intensity farming practices, cannot be known for sure. It is certainly difficult to imagine how modern hunter-gatherers would cope in Arctic regions if they did not continue to consume their high protein, high fat, animal-resourced foods, even for women throughout pregnancy [112].

Across the world, during the Upper Palaeolithic, the range of different dietary behaviours expanded according to location. In cold temperature and sub-Arctic Eurasia, populations were dependent almost entirely upon animals for food. In the tropics, populations would have existed on a much more general hunting and gathering strategy. In coastal regions and around freshwater lakes and rivers, fishing was incorporated, so that in some localities it represented the greatest component of protein in the diet [63].

Proteins

The year-round availability of meat as a food resource supported protein and energy requirements for both brain and body development, and may well have been a key factor in the dispersal of *Homo erectus* out of Africa [132]. Nowadays, protein and amino acid intake tends to be sufficient (including for most vegetarians), and the primary concerns are now associated with quality rather than quantity [111].

In most cases, the proteins in meat are far better digested and more bioavailable than the proteins in plants. For vegetarians this obviously creates some unique challenges, because it is not just the quality of different proteins that have to be sourced, but they have to eat more, gram for gram, to get the same quantity of proteins from plant foods as others would derive from meat. For those that substitute fish in place of meat this is not a problem at all, but for strict vegetarians and vegans, such restrictions within the diet need to be compensated for. Although many apes and monkeys do eat meat, the majority of their protein comes from very large amounts of plant protein, something for which our gut anatomy is not suitable (or more specifically, not in the sort of quantities required to meet our daily protein requirements) [113]. So, while over the last few million years our bodies have become far better at digesting and using meat, we still have the ability to make use of proteins from limited amounts of plants, but it would not be beneficial for our overall health to try to live off plant foods exclusively.

Meat protein is essentially identical to human proteins, meaning that it can be deposited where it is needed with virtually no modification. Meat protein is generally 95-100% digestible (98% average digestibility). Plant proteins, such as legumes and oilseed flours, show a digestibility in humans of only 84-97% (90% average digestibility). On a purely Palaeolithic diet, the average adult human would need to consume approximately 10 kg fresh weight of leafy plant foods to meet daily protein and energy demands. This would lead to an estimated dietary fibre intake of 700 grams a day [113], which is a phenomenal amount. Current recommendations are only up to about 30 grams per day. Modern vegetarians would need to

87

compensate by eating seeds, beans and legumes, but although they provide natural sources of protein, they were not eaten in significant quantities in our evolutionary past, and are not an equal substitute for meat proteins. Dietary restriction away from our natural, Palaeolithic diet, does require compensation, whether through incorporation non-Palaeolithic foods, or from supplementation. In this sense, adoption of Palaeolithic foods might be the best goal for health, rather than reverting completely to such a diet.

Modern hunter-gatherers obtain approximately 30% of their daily energy intake from protein. This equates to about three grams per kilogram of bodyweight each day for a 70 kg individual consuming 3000 kcals/day (12,500 kJ), which is well within the range observed for free-living higher primates (1.6-5.9 g/kg/day) [39]. In addition to the high-quality protein and energy, there are many essential micronutrients that are derived from animal foods [113].

Exchanging dietary carbohydrate with protein has been shown to improve blood lipid profiles by reducing LDL, VLDL and total cholesterol and triglyceride levels, whilst increasing HDL cholesterol. It is a false assumption that high amounts of animal foods necessarily cause problems with levels of blood fats. The key is to ensure that the protein intake is relatively high, the carbohydrate intake relatively low, and the spectrum of different fats is well-balanced [31]. A high protein diet may be beneficial in lessening the risk of cardiovascular disease, and improving metabolic control in type two diabetics, such as through improved glucose and insulin metabolism [31,32]. This effect is opposite to that found in individuals with a high carbohydrate diet [32].

One concern with too high an intake of protein is the negative effect on urinary calcium excretion (as mentioned in the section on Osteoporosis), and the increased risk of kidney problems. This calciuretic effect of high protein consumption may be partially related to the type of protein, such as dairy, as this effect has not been found in those that have high intakes of protein from animal sources alone. The risks of hypercalciuria include bone demineralisation and osteoporosis. Studies of pre-agricultural hunter-gatherers, however, generally show greater cortical bone cross-sectional areas, and hence greater bone robusticity and resistance to fractures, than modern humans. The difference has been associated with greater physical activity levels, which would have led to greater stress on the bones, and hence the stimulus to maintain or improve bone mineral density. Furthermore, these individuals consumed vastly more fruits and vegetables, which would have buffered the effect of the high acid intake from protein. Consequently, a high animal protein diet would appear fine, as long as it coincides with high fruit and vegetable intake, and a physically active lifestyle [31].

Homocysteine is an independent risk factor for cardiovascular disease. Meat eaters have been found to have lower blood homocysteine concentrations than non-meat eaters. Furthermore, in numerous population studies a higher blood pressure has been associated with a low protein intake [32,111]. Death rates from strokes have also been inversely related to protein intake [32]. Protein intake may also be important for the maintenance and proper functioning of the immune system, although evidence is still required to support the role of any specific amino acids. Protein restriction is only recommended for people likely to develop kidney failure due to diabetes, hypertension, or polycystic kidney disease [111].

Protein has greater than three times the thermic effect of either fat or carbohydrate, meaning that the body uses more calories to digest protein foods than the other macronutrients. This in itself may be good reason to recommend higher protein diets for those wanting to lose weight. Recent research findings have found that a high protein diet is better than a high carbohydrate diet for promoting and maintaining weight loss, while producing less hunger and more satisfaction [32].

In many westernised countries, there are health concerns regarding the fat composition of domesticated livestock, which tends to be much higher in saturated fats than wild ungulates (hooved mammals, including cattle, deer and pigs), making it difficult to suggest that adopting a meat intake similar to that of our Palaeolithic ancestors will automatically confer health benefits. Furthermore, there are concerns regarding potentially negative health consequences of eating meat from animals administered with various steroids and antibiotics [113]. Wild meats, wild fowl and free range, organic meats would be our best available options nowadays.

Fats

Similar to carnivores, as humans we are very inefficient at modifying some of the fats that we eat, into the essential fats that our body requires. As with our requirement for vitamin C, our inefficiency at producing essential fatty acids comes from the fact that we used to ingest sufficient quantities in our past, and so any adaptation to manufacture our own would have been surplus to requirements. Thus, we cannot manufacture essential fats because we never needed to before. As with the carnivores, the essential fats that we required were sourced from animal foods, with plants containing the sort of fats that needed to be modified [31]. Hence, as our ancestors relied less on plant foods and more on animal foods, so our need to modify plant fats into essential ones was reduced.

The absolute amount of fat within a wild animal is dependent upon its body mass. A larger animal will tend to have a higher percentage of body fat than a smaller animal. Furthermore, body fat percentages in wild animals vary according to age, sex and season. Thus, peak body fat levels in wild animals are only maintained for a few months of the year, regardless of where in the world the animals live [32].

In mammals, overeating leads to the storage of surplus energy in fat stores (adipocytes). The types of fats found stored in the body differ by location. In wild mammals, most excess fat is stored around the stomach (abdominal fat) and beneath the skin (subcutaneous fat). More than half of the stored fat in adipocytes is in the form of saturated fats (saturated fatty acids, or SFAs). Around muscle tissue and other organs it is in the form of unsaturated fats (either monounsaturated fats, MUFAs, or polyunsaturated fatty acids, PUFAs) [32].

Due to the fact that abdominal and subcutaneous fats are depleted during most of the year in wild animals, the majority of fats remaining in the carcass are monounsaturated and polyunsaturated. This demonstrates that throughout our past, for the majority of the year, we would have eaten mainly unsaturated fats. When we selectively butchered carcasses, the lean muscle meat would often be discarded (as it contains less nutritional value than organ meats), but still the mono- and polyunsaturated fats would have accounted for the majority of fats ingested, throughout most of the year [32].

When we began to domesticate animals, we were able to prevent these seasonal fluctuations in body fat levels, which led animals to have higher saturated fat levels, and this would be throughout the year rather than for just a few months. Furthermore, it meant that animals could always be slaughtered when at peak fat percentage. Not only since the Neolithic were our animal foods always high in saturated fats, but also we used preservation techniques to store produce rich in saturated fats for prolonged periods of time, often in the form of cheese, butter, tallow and salted fatty meats. This permitted a high intake of saturated fats throughout the year [32].

Following the Industrial Revolution, technological advances such as the steam engine, railways, and mechanical farming devices, allowed for an increase in grain harvests and a greater efficiency of transport, both of grain and of cattle. The combination of these factors led to the practice of grain-feeding cattle. Prior to 1850 in the U.S., virtually all cattle was free-range or pasture fed, and was typically slaughtered at around four or five years of age. By approximately 1885, the science and technology had developed to facilitate the growth of 545-kg steers that could be ready for slaughter in twenty-four months. The meat in these animals would often be 'marbled', a trait rarely found in pasture-fed, free range or wild animals, and comes from the excessive accumulation of fats within the muscles. This meat is particularly high in saturated fats, with a lower proportion of omega-three and higher proportion of omega-six fatty acids. Since the 1950s, the technology has developed further, and now obese (greater than 30% bodyfat) cattle can be brought to slaughter at fourteen months. Approximately 99% of all beef now consumed in the U.S. has been farmed in this manner, with the high SFAs, low omega-three and high omega-six fats [32].

There are three main categories of fats, or rather of fatty acids. They are the saturated fatty acids (SFAs), monounsaturated fatty acids (MUFAs), and polyunsaturated fatty acids (PUFAs). Further, the essential polyunsaturated fatty acids occur in two groups, the omega-three fatty acids and the omega-six fatty acids [32]. A wealth of research into dietary fats has been undertaken due to the association of fat with various diseases and ill health [127]. Fats can be described further according to their chemical structure, as being either *cis* or *trans* fats. *Cis* fats are those that primarily occur in nature, and what we are used to ingesting from natural foods. *Trans* fats do occur in small amounts in nature, but mostly they are formed when vegetable oils are chemically altered, such as through hydrogenation or through repeated cooking/heating. Vegetable oils were never intended for use in cooking, and the formation of *trans* fats has been linked with more adverse effects on cholesterol than saturated fats, and may even be linked to fertility problems. *Trans* fats can be found in hydrogenated foods, such as margarine, and in processed and baked foods. Consequently, substantial evidence now exists that it is the type of fat that is more important in the prevention of chronic diseases, rather than the total amount of fat [32].

The mono- and polyunsaturated fats are regarded as health-promoting, whereas most saturated and *trans* fats are regarded as detrimental to health when consumed in excessive quantities. Furthermore, it is the balance of omega-three to omega-six polyunsaturated fats that plays an integral role in preventing chronic disease and promoting good health. Our westernised diets often contain excessive saturated and *trans* fats, and insufficient omega-threes in relation to omega-sixes [32].

In the U.S., during the ninety years between 1909 and 1999, oils used for cooking and salads increased by 130% per capita, shortening consumption increased by 140%, and margarine consumption increased by 410%. Oils have been made from plant foods for over 5000 years. With the exception of olive oil, most oils were previously used for illumination, lubrication and medicine [32]. The concept of making and cooking food with these oils is actually quite novel.

High dietary intakes of saturated and *trans* fats elevate blood concentrations of total and LDL cholesterol (explained in following section), thereby increasing the risk of cardiovascular disease (CVD) [32,182]. Diets rich in saturated fatty acids are also associated with an increased risk of ventricular fibrillation and sudden cardiac death in primates, whilst diets high in polyunsaturated fats are protective [133]. Omega-three fatty acids are associated with a reduced risk of CVD.

There are a number of ways in which omega-threes may prevent CVD, including via a reduction in ventricular arrhythmias, blood pressure, blood clotting, blood fat concentrations, and by the prevention or limitation of the growth of atherosclerotic plaques. High dietary intakes of omega-threes are also associated with preventing or ameliorating many inflammatory and autoimmune diseases [32]. Both omega-three and omega-six fatty acid consumption is inversely related to the risk of coronary heart disease (CHD). Two polyunsaturated fats, eicosapentaenoic acid (EPA) and docosahexaenoic acid (DHA), found principally in fish and some vegetable oils, have been shown to reduce the risk of coronary and all cause mortality [133].

In one study, both low fat and high fat diets with identical ratios of the different fats, showed no differences in effect on total and LDL cholesterol levels. This reinforces the notion that it is the type of fat, rather than the quantity of fat, which is most important for affecting health [182].

The six major sources of saturated fatty acids in westernised diets are fatty meats, baked goods, cheese, milk, margarine and butter. Of these, only fatty meats would have been present in the diets of our Palaeolithic ancestors, and then only for a few months of the year. Our ancestors that lived prior to the Neolithic would have enjoyed diets high in the unsaturated fats (MUFAs and PUFAs), with high levels of saturated fats occurring only for a limited period during the year. The SFAs that were in the diet would not have been in sufficient quantities, for long enough periods of time, to have any effect on our health as a species [32].

The oil-seed processing industry commenced at the beginning of the 20th century. The result of this was a significant increase in our intakes of vegetable fats, which directly increased our omega-six levels, at the expense of lowering omega-three intake (vegetable fats are inherently higher in omega-sixes than omega-threes) [32]. This ratio has then been exacerbated due to the growing norm of eating meat from grain-fed cattle over the past 100 years. In the U.S., the current ratio of omega-six to omega-three fatty acids is approximately 10:1, whereas the ratio for hunter-gatherers and ancestral humans is estimated to be between 2:1 and 3:1 [32,39].

Hydrogenation, the process used to make liquid vegetable fats behave more like solid fats, thereby allowing the manufacture of margarine, shortening, and various hydrogenated-fat-containing foods, was invented in 1897 [32]. The hydrogenation process introduced a novel *trans* fat into the human diet, which elevates blood cholesterol concentrations and leads to an increased risk of CVD [32,182], even more than the intake of saturated fats [133]. *Trans* fats also reduce HDL cholesterol levels, thereby increasing the LDL cholesterol ratio, and are considered more atherogenic than saturated fats [133]. In the U.S., consumption of *trans* fatty acids accounts for an estimated 7.4% of the total fats in the diet [32]. The process of hydrogenation also removes essential fatty acids [133].

Trans fats do occur in nature and would have been ingested by early humans, both from breast milk, and from some herbivore meats. With these particular *trans* fats, they would have been broken down during digestion, and there is some evidence to suggest that they could even have had anti-carcinogenic and anti-atherogenic properties. The proportion of these is small in relation to all of the types of *trans* fats now consumed by Americans [39] and other people in westernised populations.

Considerable attention has focussed on a possible link between dietary fat and colon cancer. However, recent research has shown that certain unsaturated fats are protective against the cancer. Specifically, olive oil and fish oil have both been shown to exhibit an anti-carcinogenic effect, when compared with safflower oil [13].

Cholesterol

37 million American adults maintain high-risk total cholesterol levels of over 240 mg/dl [32], whereas modern hunter-gatherers have levels averaging 125 mg/dl, similar to that of free-living non-human primates [40]. Hypercholesterolaemia is a key factor in the inception and progression of coronary heart disease (CHD). Whereas societies with the hunter-gatherer range of cholesterol levels have an incredibly low incidence of CHD, modern westernised populations with their average levels above 200 mg/dl have CHD as the single leading cause of mortality [40]. A 10% reduction in plasma cholesterol has been associated with a 25% reduction in the incidence of CHD after five years. A reduction in serum LDL cholesterol of 1.6 mmol/l has been associated with a 51% reduction in CHD events two or more years later. The evidence shows that the greater the reduction in LDL cholesterol, and the longer the period of reduction, the greater is the reduction in CHD events. Importantly, there is no age at which the benefits of reducing cholesterol have not been shown [182].

Cholesterol is a fatty substance that we have in our blood and that is an essential component of cell membranes. Cholesterol has to be bound onto proteins (lipoproteins) to be transported around the body. Cholesterol produced by the liver emerges in the form of either very low-density lipoprotein (VLDL) cholesterol, or high-density lipoproteins (HDL). VLDL cholesterol is subsequently metabolised into low-density lipoprotein (LDL) cholesterol. It is a high ratio of LDL to HDL cholesterol that is associated with ill health and disease. HDL acts as a cholesterol scavenger, and takes in cholesterol from the artery walls and returns it to the liver [191].

As concentrations of total and LDL cholesterol increase so does the risk of cardiovascular disease (CVD) [182]. As mentioned previously, someone with low LDL cholesterol levels will almost certainly not have a myocardial infarction [128]. The evidence that links dietary fat with serum cholesterol concentrations is incontrovertible [40]. The key fats responsible are the saturated and *trans* fats [32,40]. For our distant ancestors, saturated fats would have constituted approximately 5% of total daily energy intake, with the intake of *trans* fats being negligible. Saturated fat intake by modern Americans is approximately three-times higher than that of our Palaeolithic ancestors [40]. *Trans* fat consumption from hydrogenated vegetable fats and oils is now ubiquitous. Monounsaturated and polyunsaturated fats are hypocholesterolaemic, that is, they can actually reduce blood cholesterol levels [31], but they are being consumed far less than would have been the case for our Palaeolithic ancestors.

Astonishingly, our hunter-gatherer ancestors ingested approximately 480 mg of cholesterol per day (well above the current recommended intake of 300 mg per day), due to the high intake of animal foods, yet their actual serum cholesterol levels would have been slightly less than the low levels recommended for high-risk CHD patients. Thus, dietary cholesterol itself is not a major independent factor for increasing serum cholesterol levels [39].

The protective effects of HDL cholesterol have become apparent from the research undertaken, with the ratio of total to HDL cholesterol being a strong predictor of CHD [128,133]. Replacing saturated fat intake with other fats reduces the total:HDL cholesterol ratio, but replacing SFAs with carbohydrates does not [133]. The omega-three fatty acids found in fish oils have been found to increase HDL cholesterol [182], and thereby reduce the risk of CHD [128]. Regular aerobic exercise, weight loss (especially in individuals with abdominal obesity), consuming niacin-rich foods and smoking cessation have all been shown to have positive effects on improving HDL cholesterol levels [121].

Dairy fat and meat are major dietary sources of cholesterol [133]. Regardless of how lean animal meat might be, all cell membranes contain cholesterol [39]. Eggs are particularly rich in cholesterol content, but unlike dairy and animal sources, they do not contain saturated fats. If there are limitations in saturated fat intake, then there need be no severe restriction of egg intake [133], although current recommendations are for no more than one a day.

Studies have found that *trans* fats are even worse than saturated fats. They are more atherogenic, and they not only increase LDL cholesterol, but they reduce HDL cholesterol too. Thus, *trans* fats encourage a worse cholesterol profile than saturated fats, thereby presenting a greater risk for developing CHD. Public health strategies

96

should focus on eliminating *trans* fats from processed foods, and educating both children and adults about the risks. In many countries *trans* fats have been eliminated from retail fats and spreads, but deep-fried fast foods and baked goods are a major and growing source [133].

High glycaemic load carbohydrates (discussed later) also promote an atherogenic cholesterol profile, by elevating LDL cholesterol and reducing HDL cholesterol. These carbohydrates increase the risk of cardiovascular disease (CVD) not just through the effects on cholesterol levels, but also by increasing the concentrations of a particular protein (C-reactive protein), which is an even stronger predictor of CVD than LDL cholesterol. Conversely, fruit and vegetable intake is associated with reductions in total and LDL cholesterol. This effect is greater than simply reducing saturated fat intake alone [32].

Brain Development

The brain contains approximately 600 grams of fat per kilogram of total weight [24]. Animal fats have been an essential source of a number of polyunsaturated fatty acids, including omega-six arachidonic acid (AA) and docosatetraenoic acid (DTA), and omega-three docosahexaenoic acid (DHA). These three fatty acids make up over 90% of the polyunsaturated fats found in the grey matter of all mammalian brains. The availability of these fats in the appropriate ratios, combined with increasing social complexity, allowed our cranial capacity to become three times that of our australopithecine ancestors [40].

It might not be best to take our larger brains for granted. Since our brain capacity peaked in the Late Palaeolithic, we have seen a reduction in capacity of approximately 11%. This diminution has paralleled our diminished intake of the preformed, long-chain polyunsaturated fats, which we used to obtain in sufficient quantities from animal fat [40] and freshwater fish and shellfish [24]. An abundant and balanced intake of these fatty acids has been an absolute requirement for sustaining the very rapid expansion of the human cerebral cortex over the last one to two million years [24]. Whilst we can manufacture these required fats internally, the process appears to be too slow to supply the quantities and types of fats needed for optimal brain growth [40,115], especially during foetal development and infancy [40]. Deficiencies during infant development can result in an irreversible failure to accomplish certain specific components of brain growth [24].

Our current deficiency of DHA, brought about by dietary changes in the last century [115] is particularly important because our intake of omega-six fatty acids inhibits the formation of DHA [40]. It is clearly tempting to speculate about a relationship between our inappropriate ratios of these fats, together with our decreased consumption of animal fats, and our decreasing cranial capacity. Furthermore, the imbalance between these fats could be related to the prevalence of depression, which is a debilitating disorder responsible for more disability-related 'lost years' than heart attacks, lung cancer or AIDS [40]. Our sub-clinical omega-three deficiency has also been linked to cardiovascular disease, inflammatory disorders, other mental and psychiatric disorders, and sub-optimal neural development [115].

Studies have found a relationship between high ratios of omega-six to omega-three fatty acids and depression. There is a direct association between higher ratios and more frequent and more severe depressive episodes. Since the industrial revolution, omega-six intake has soared relative to omega-three intake, due primarily to increased vegetable oil consumption and the use of corn-feeding livestock [40]. The fatty acid profile of wild game animals is far higher in preferable polyunsaturated fats than commercial livestock, and our ancestors could have had up to ten times more of these fats than we have in our contemporary diets [39]. Fish, on the other hand, is a good sources of omega-threes and national fish consumption is inversely related to national rates of depression [40]. Increased omega-three intake is associated with a reduced risk of mortality from cardiovascular diseases, improved neonatal neurodevelopment, and lower blood pressure later in life [115].

Bone marrow and brain tissue are rich sources of both AA and DHA, whereas liver and muscle tissues are good sources of AA and moderate sources of DHA [94,134]. Freshwater fish and seafood are also good sources of AA and DHA [94,107]. We have evidence that both meat and fish consumption increased approximately two million years ago, with the earliest evidence of our own species and tool use being associated with aquatic resource bases [24]. Many of our ancestral populations lived along waterways and near coastal regions, and their migration routes may have kept them close to water throughout their lives. The archaeological evidence suggests that our ancestors exploited fish and other aquatic foods more than we had previously realised [107]. Tropical freshwater fish and shellfish have polyunsaturated lipid profiles more similar to those of the human brain than any other food source known [24]. Birds, small mammals, reptiles and amphibians that ate aquatic foods may have also provided us with adequate DHA when we, in turn, ate them [26].

Plant Foods

Our theories regarding human foraging activity prior to the Neolithic can be substantiated through archaeological finds [54]. One particularly well-preserved collection of plant remains has been found along the shores of the Sea of Galilee, in modern-day Israel. The site was used by humans 23,000 years ago, and yielded over 90,000 plant remains, including grass seeds, cereals (emmer wheat and barley), acorns, almonds, raspberries, grapes, wild fig, pistachios, and a number and variety of other fruits and berries. Due to the excellent preservation of the site, 142 different species of plants were identified, indicating a rich diversity of sources of fibre consumed by the people living there at that time [90].

In Australia, Aborigines are known to have included some 300 different species of fruit, 150 different varieties of roots and tubers, and vast numbers of different nuts, seeds and vegetables. The analysis of more than 800 of these plant foods led to the finding that the Aborigines were consuming between 80 and 130 grams of fibre per day. The actual amount of fibre varied according to how much plant material was consumed each day, as a proportion of total food intake. Even the total figures though do not represent the highest quantities of fibre ingested each day, as the researchers did not measure certain types of fibre found within the roots and tubers [90].

Similarly, an almost continuous 10,000-year record of the foraging lifestyle of native North Americans has been found within cave deposits. The remains were again well-preserved, and their extensive analysis showed that the people living there had consumed between 150 and 250 grams of fibre each day, coming from dozens of different species of plants. Almost all of the human coprolites studied revealed undigested fibre (cellulose), throughout the entire 10,000-year history, demonstrating how fibre-rich these individuals were [90].

Of particular importance amongst the North Americans, was their consumption of plant foods that contained certain types of molecules and insoluble fibres, which are known to enhance the bacterial profile of the colon. This, in turn, would have had positive effects in terms of the production of important fats, reduction in acidity, and the conversion of bile acids, and would have had a strong impact on gut health. Modern populations, by contrast, are more likely to ingest far less fibre overall, and types of fibre that are likely to be fermented much faster, which is far less healthy and far more likely to allow cancers to develop in the gut [90].

The domesticated fleshy fruits that we find in our supermarkets nowadays are typically attractive in appearance, have considerable succulent pulp, and few or no seeds. The reason for all of this is that they have been selectively bred to appear that way, in addition to which they are also very sweet. Their naturally occurring, wild fruit counterparts tend to have a higher ratio of seeds to pulp, a less pronounced sweet taste, and often an unappealing appearance. However, the ancestors of these fruits were those that were consumed by our human ancestors, and by the ancestors of the modern primates. Hence, our bodies evolved on a diet that included wild fruits, similar if not identical, to those found in tropical forests. Cultivated fruits are yet another newcomer to our modern diets [113].

One of the key differences between wild and cultivated fruits is the *type* of sugar in the pulps. Wild fruits tend to be very high in glucose and contain some fructose. Cultivated fruits, by contrast, are typically highest in sucrose. Sucrose is commonly obtained from sugar cane for the manufacture of table sugar, and for sweetening confectionery, cakes, biscuits, etc. Cultivated fruits are therefore a chemically different food to the wild fruits eaten by modern-day apes and other primates. The reason that they are so high in sucrose is because of careful selection to reproduce the sweetest fruits grown, which has significantly altered the nature of the fruit over many generations [113]. Again, our evolutionary adaptations took place when we were eating wild fruits, and we are not physiologically able to effectively deal with high concentrations of sucrose in our diets.

Wild fruits are also higher in fibre, protein, woody seeds, essential micronutrients, and other key nutrients. Further, and not necessarily a pleasant thought for all, wild fruits are more likely to contain tiny insects and larvae, which could be a good source of vitamin B_{12}. Wild fruits also contain considerable amounts of vitamin C. Cultivated fruits, which might look and taste more pleasant, are regarded as being less nutritious than their wild relatives. It is also

101

likely that they place a greater stress on our physiology [113], which could be evidenced in conditions such as type two diabetes mellitus. Any such stress, however, would most probably pale into insignificance next to the physiological stresses elicited by the high consumption of processed sugars, such as those found in confectionary, cakes, soft drinks, ice cream, and so on.

Vitamin C is a particularly interesting substance for us. Unlike most mammals, all monkeys, apes and humans (tested up to the year 1999) have been found to lack an enzyme essential for the manufacture of vitamin C. This was clearly not an issue for us in our evolutionary past, as we must have been consuming so much vitamin C in our diets that there was simply no need to manufacture that particular chemical within us. Our closest living relatives, the great apes (chimpanzees, bonobos, gorillas and orangutans), consume diets that contain from two to six grams of vitamin C per day, depending on species and sex. Our recommended daily intake is currently only about 60 *milligrams* per day. It is likely that our vitamin C requirement would have been less than those of the other apes, as plant foods would have comprised a much smaller percentage of our diet, but taking into account our size this may still have been measured in grams rather than milligrams. It should be stressed that this vitamin C came from an abundance of plant foods, and so it would not be prudent to use supplements to counter any current deficits. Vitamin C is an essential nutrient for us to obtain from fruit, but equally there are various other important nutrients that we can also obtain from fruit, such as vitamin E, pro-vitamin A, vitamin K and folic acid, as well as various minerals such as copper, iron, sodium and calcium, and up to thousands of other beneficial phytochemicals. Unsurprisingly, such nutrients are found in greater concentrations in wild fruits than cultivated ones [113]. Supplements may contain the wrong forms, have low bioavailability, promote nutrient imbalances, and have nowhere near the vast quantities and types of nutrients as those obtained from consuming a variety of fresh fruit.

Again, it is important to stress the importance of plant foods in the diet. These are a key source of energy, essential nutrients, and fibre. One of the downfalls of modern society is that our diets can contain over 70% refined foods and foods that we are not physiologically adapted to deal with effectively. This manifests itself as disease and ill-health. The lack of optimal nutrient content in cultivated fruits simply reinforces the importance of having a varied diet, comprising many different plant foods. It would be wise to avoid reliance upon a high-cultivated fruit intake to account for *all* plant foods consumed.

Eating a variety of different plant foods is important, and not only to be sure of consuming a wide range of healthy nutrients. Plants do not desire to be eaten. If plants were to nurture some desire, then quite possibly in kin with most living organisms, then that desire would be to reproduce. In most instances being eaten would represent a barrier to success. There are some exceptions, such as nuts and seeds that are not digested by animals in nature, but instead pass through the gut and emerge at the other end surrounded by fertile, nutrient-rich excrement, thus allowing an excellent environment in which the young seed can grow. On the whole, however, plants tend to defend themselves.

In accordance with the plants' requirement to reproduce, it defends itself with a number of bioactive substances, such as terpenoids, alkaloids, glucosinolates, tannins, phytoestrogens and lectins. Many, or most, of these substances constitute the plants' defence mechanism against the herbivores. The highest concentration of bioactive substances is typically found in seeds and beans, which would not have constituted a significant part of our ancestors' diet. What we should be aiming to do, therefore, is to eat a large variety of plant foods, which keeps the dietary concentration of any one bioactive substance low. This is what we find with modern hunter-gatherers, and what we have evidence for in the archaeology [96].

Carbohydrates

Americans currently obtain approximately 50% of their daily energy from carbohydrates, of which approximately 15% is added sugars (from processing, preparation, etc.) [39]. Carbohydrates are thought to have contributed to approximately 35% of the total daily energy intake of our Palaeolithic ancestors. Of this, no more than a couple of kilograms per year might have been honey [32,39], which is the closest Palaeolithic food to our modern, refined sugar [39], and even that would have been only seasonally available. A consequence of this is that westernised populations are now consuming refined sugars in unprecedented quantities, and this is a phenomenon to which our physiology and digestive anatomy has not become adapted [32].

Worldwide, the consumption of refined sugar has increased dramatically since the Industrial Revolution. In England, the *per capita* refined sugar consumption rose from 6.8 kg in 1815 to 54.5 kg in 1970. Similarly, sugar consumption has continued to increase over the past thirty years, with *per capita* figures in the U.S. rising from 55.5 kg in 1970 to 69.1 kg in 2000 [32].

Following a meal, both fat and muscle are stimulated by the rise in insulin levels, and both take up glucose into their cells from the blood. The capacity for muscle to take up glucose is far higher than that of fat, for any given weight. The problem is that, by comparison to our distant ancestors, we are generally fatter and have a lot less muscle tissue. Our ability to maintain carbohydrate homeostasis evolved over the millions of years of our pasts, throughout which our body compositions were very different from what they are now. What this means is that following a carbohydrate-rich meal, the insulin that is released is often insufficient to restore normal blood glucose levels, because of our body compositions. This means that additional insulin must then be released from the pancreas. Over the long-term, this can lead to problems with glucose tolerance and then to diabetes [40]. Thus, the combinations of high carbohydrate meals, high body fat, and low muscle mass (compounded by a lack of exercise), means that the body struggles to maintain its natural homeostasis. All of these factors are a direct result of our modern lifestyles and contemporary diets. They are not factors to which our physiology evolved, and consequently we will always be at risk of diabetes for as long as we continue to live sedentary lifestyles, increase our body fat levels, and eat high-carbohydrate meals.

The largest sources of carbohydrates in our contemporary diets are cereal grains, with dairy products representing the second largest source. Our ancestors would have consumed hardly any cereal grains, and no dairy products after weaning. Fruits and vegetables used to comprise most of the carbohydrate content of our diets, but they now represent only about 23% [39].

If we were to eliminate added sugar from our diets, then the carbohydrate contribution to daily energy would be equivalent to that of our distant ancestors. We would then need to exchange the cereal grains and dairy foods with fruits and vegetables, so as to reach a more qualitative equivalent [39].

Another important consideration is that of the effects of high carbohydrate consumption on risk factors for cardiovascular disease (CVD). General advice has been to replace saturated fats with carbohydrates, but studies have found that this creates unfavourable blood lipid profiles, including a reduction in HDL cholesterol whilst elevating VLDL and LDL cholesterol and triglyceride levels [31,133]. Carbohydrate intake should be maintained at natural levels, and with regard to the prevention of cardiovascular disease, the evidence suggests that it is far more prudent to replace saturated fats with unsaturated ones, rather than with carbohydrates. This approach has been found to lower LDL cholesterol levels, without having an adverse effect on the other blood lipids. Additionally, it has been suggested that foods with a high glycaemic load and low fibre content increase the risk of both CVD and type two diabetes [31], both due to the effects of such foods on blood glucose regulation [133].

Fruit and vegetable consumption is inversely related to the risk of ischaemic heart disease and stroke, and has been shown to lower blood pressure. The lowest risks are related to high consumption of cruciferous vegetables (such as brussels sprouts, cabbage and cauliflower), green leafy vegetables, citrus fruits, and vegetables. The contribution of fruits and vegetables to cardiovascular health is attributable to a variety of phytonutrients, potassium and fibre [133], again supporting the notion that it is the consumption of a variety of fruits and vegetables that is the key, rather than attempts to self-correct insufficiencies through supplementation. Conversely, refined sugars are essentially devoid of vitamins and minerals, making them 'empty' of any nutritional benefit other than basic energy. A consequence of this is that increasing reliance on refined sugars is driving down vitamin and mineral status, especially as the sugars are being taken in place of fruits and vegetables [32].

Fibre

Fibre is required for over 40 actions within the digestive system [52]. Two of the major constituents of dietary fibre are cellulose and hemicellulose. No mammal, including humans, is known to produce the enzymes necessary to degrade them [113]. Instead, humans along with the other mammals, have anaerobic bacteria and other gut flora, in various areas along the digestive tract, which can carry out this function. The result is that the fibre passes relatively intact into the large intestine, where it is broken down through a process of fermentation, and fatty acids are then released that can then be absorbed through the gut [39,52,133].

Interestingly, although not necessarily surprisingly, we are very efficient at degrading the fibres found in most fruits and vegetables, but very inefficient at degrading fibres from cereal grains, such as wheat bran [39,113]. Additionally, fruits contain twice the amount of fibre as whole grains, and whole grains contain four times the amount of fibre of refined grains. Non-starchy vegetables would appear to be best though, containing eight times more fibre than whole grains. The fibre-depleted refined grains account for 85% of the grains consumed in the U.S. [32]. Non-starchy vegetables are basically all vegetables other than grain foods, roots and potatoes.

Flowering plants can be divided into two groups. Monocots are flowering plants that produce seeds and one seed leaf, whereas dicots are flowering plants that produce two seed leaves. That might not be particularly helpful when shopping, but as a guide the following table separates some of the more common plant foods. Most fruits, vegetables and flowers are dicot plants, which happen to be the traditional foods of the anthropoids. As anthropoids ourselves, we too are very efficient at degrading dicot plants, but our digestive kinetics and fermentation efficiencies are not able to effectively break down the fibres from monocot plants [113].

Table 3.0. Comparison of various monocot and dicot plant foods

Monocot	Dicot	
Asparagus	Apples	Beans
Banana	Broccoli	Cabbage
Barley	Carrot	Cauliflower
Coconut	Celery	Clover
Corn	Legumes (all)	Oil Seeds
Garlic	Parsley	Peaches
Ginger	Peanuts	Pears
Maize	Peas	Peppers
Millet	Plums	Potatoes
Oats	Roots	Rosemary
Onion	Sage	Soybeans
Pineapple	Spices	Thyme
Rice	Tomatoes	Tubers
Rye	Turnips	Woody Plants
Wheat		
Yam		

Furthermore, and still no doubt unsurprisingly, there are vast differences between the fibre contents of wild and cultivated plant foods. An analysis of the uncultivated fruits and vegetables consumed by modern hunter-gatherers found that the average fibre content of the foods was 133 grams per kilogram of total weight. Commercially available fruits and vegetables contain a miserly 42 grams per kilo. Hence, not only were our Palaeolithic ancestors consuming significantly more fruits and vegetables than we are, but also their fibre intake represented a far higher proportion of their diet than it does for us [39].

Compounding the issue of how to raise fibre consumption, some types of fibre adversely affect mineral bioavailability, especially when a chemical called phytate is present. Phytic acid is a prominent constituent of many cereal grains, but is barely present, if present at all, in most uncultivated fruits and vegetables. Therefore, not only do our contemporary diets not contain enough fibre, what is there often constitutes the wrong type of fibre, even to the point of compromising mineral availability [39].

Some dietary fibres, primarily those found in fruits and vegetables, are known to reduce both total and LDL cholesterol levels, without negatively affecting HDL cholesterol levels [32,133]. The reduction in total cholesterol, from shifting fibre intake to fruit and vegetable sources, is usually between 5-10% [133]. Realistically, some of the benefits found in the studies may be attributable to other constituents of the foods consumed, rather than just fibre alone [52]. Fibre may influence health in other ways, as inadequate dietary fibre may be responsible for initiating or exacerbating constipation, appendicitis, haemorrhoids, deep vein thrombosis, varicose veins, diverticulitis, hiatal hernia, and gastrointestinal reflux [32].

The argument in support of a more natural, evolutionary-biased diet, and the avoidance of functional foods, can use supplemental fibre as a case in point. One of the main problems with several fibre supplements is that they are fermented too rapidly. This could lead to a huge surge in microbial activity, but the microbes would soon become depleted and then either starve or start causing damage to each other or to the lining of the gut. It is unlikely that such a scenario could be beneficial. What this comes down to is that the interactions of diet and gut health are many and varied, and one should be wary of over-simplistic solutions, involving supplements or other function-designed foods [52]. Furthermore, approximately 60% of faecal matter is bacterial, some of which has the potential to be harmful [56]. Sufficient fibre is therefore required to ensure that faecal matter passes efficiently through the intestine.

For all of these reasons it is recommended that dietary fibre should come from a variety of fruits and vegetables, rather than supplemental sources [133]. Diets free from cereal grains, dairy products, refined oil and sugars, or processed foods have been shown to contain significantly more fibre than the typical, westernised diets, and more fibre than the currently estimated minimum requirements for health [32].

Glycaemic Index and Glycaemic Load

The glycaemic index was originally developed in 1981, as a tool to compare the effects of different foods on blood glucose levels. In 1997, the glycaemic index was superseded by the concept of glycaemic load (glycaemic index multiplied by the carbohydrate content for a given serving size) [32], as a means of quantifying the effect of carbohydrate foods on blood glucose levels [180]. Glycaemic load has become a more useful tool, as it specifically deals with both the quality and quantity of dietary carbohydrate, and creates a very different list to the glycaemic index [32]. In fact, a study published in 2006 showed that the glycaemic index alone is unable to predict the effect of carbohydrates on blood glucose, when different amounts of carbohydrates are consumed. The same study confirmed support for the use of glycaemic load instead [47], although some refinements of the calculations used to determine glycaemic load are still required [180]. In short, there are currently two methods that are used for estimating the effect of a given food on blood glucose levels, and neither of them is wholly reliable. Glycaemic load takes into account an estimate of serving sizes, but the greater the effect of the food on blood glucose, the less accurate the estimated glycaemic load becomes. Further studies, including improvements in the manner in which glycaemic load is calculated, should make this a far superior tool in years to come.

Table 4.0. Table for Comparison of Glycaemic Index (G.I) versus Glycaemic Load (G.L.) [187,188, 189, 190]

High G.I.	High G.L.
Breads	Cereals
Cereals	Couscous
Jacket Potato	Crisps
Mashed Potato	Pasta
Parsnips	Snickers Bar
Suede	Sugar-sweetened beverages
Watermelon	Sweets
White Rice	White Rice
Medium G.I.	**Medium G.L.**
Basmati Rice	Apple Juice
Biscuits	Brown Rice
Boiled Potato	Fettuccini
Cantaloupe	New Potatoes
Coca Cola	Orange Juice
Honey	Pizza
Ice Cream	Sweet Potatoes
Pineapple	Wild Rice
Wholemeal Bread	Yoghurt
Low G.I.	**Low G.L.**
Apples	Apples
Bananas	Cantaloupe
Cherries	Carrots
Crisps	Grapefruit
Grapefruit	Grapes
Grapes	High Fibre Fruits and Vegetables
Lentils	Ice Cream
Milk	Legumes
Orange Juice	Oranges
Oranges	Peaches
Pasta	Peanuts
Peanuts	Pineapple
Porridges	Strawberries
Snickers Bar	Sucrose
Strawberries	Sweetcorn
Sweetcorn	White Bread
Yoghurt	Wholemeal Bread

Please note that the Glycaemic Load incorporates suggested serving sizes. Ice cream, for example, has a serving size of 72 grams (1 cup)

111

Once blood glucose levels have risen following a meal, insulin release is then stimulated to facilitate the uptake of glucose into fat and muscle tissue. By consuming a diet in which high glycaemic load foods are repeatedly eaten during the day, average daily blood glucose and insulin levels are higher, than if ingesting the same number of calories through low glycaemic load foods. Long-term, this can lead to adverse effects on health and metabolism. Insulin resistance, resulting from the repeated release of insulin from the pancreas, leads to hyperinsulinaemia, in which insulin is chronically higher in the blood as it is being continuously stimulated to remove glucose. This is the primary metabolic defect in the metabolic syndrome [32].

Metabolic syndrome is associated with obesity, coronary heart disease, type two diabetes mellitus, hypertension, and dyslipidaemia (elevated LDL cholesterol and triacylglycerols and reduced HDL cholesterol). The metabolic syndrome may extend to other chronic illnesses and conditions that are prevalent in westernised societies, including myopia, acne, gout, polycystic ovary syndrome, epithelial cell cancers (breast, colon, prostate), male vertex balding, skin tags and acanthosis nigricans [32]. A study of refined sugar consumption in Italy, found that total refined cereal foods comprise approximately 40% of total daily energy intake. They also found that there was a link between glycaemic load and increased risk of myocardial infarction, but only amongst certain at-risk groups, such as the elderly and the overweight [162]. Diseases associated with insulin resistance are either rare or absent in modern hunter-gatherer and less westernised populations, all with more traditional dietary and lifestyle habits [32]. Amongst diabetics, good glycaemic control has been shown to prevent the microvascular complications associated with the disease. Good glycaemic control also reduces the risk of stroke [182].

Refined grain and sugar products nearly always maintain much higher glycaemic loads that unprocessed fruits and vegetables. The unrefined, wild plant foods available to our Palaeolithic ancestors typically elicit a low glycaemic load. Despite milk, yoghurt and ice cream having relatively low glycaemic loads, they are considered to be highly insulinotropic. That is, they stimulate a greater insulin release than would be anticipated on the basis of their carbohydrate

112

content. Fructose has a similar effect. This is one of the pitfalls of measuring glucose response, and relying on that as a sole measure for prescribing types of carbohydrates. People ought to be aware of the exceptions (such as dairy foods and fructose), although these foods are naturally absent from a diet based on that of our Palaeolithic ancestors.

High quantities of fructose are actually used in laboratory rodents to induce insulin resistance. Much lower concentrations of fructose have been shown to worsen insulin sensitivity in hyperinsulinaemic men, and it has recently been found that fructose can induce insulin resistance in men and women [32]. Although fructose ('fruit sugar') occurs naturally (as does sucrose), it is usually in relatively small quantities. Recently it has been made available as processed sugar to be used in place of sucrose. The logic behind producing such a product is that it is significantly sweeter than sucrose, and can therefore be used in smaller quantities.

In the typical U.S. diet, high glycaemic load sugars account for 18.6% of total energy, and refined cereal grains, also with high glycaemic loads, account for 20.4%. Hence, at least 39% of the US diet's total energy intake comes from foods that promote insulin resistance. Such foods were rarely, if ever, consumed by the average American as recently as 200 years ago. Not only are the high glycaemic load foods associated with insulin resistance, but they may also encourage atherosclerosis. The indirect association is due to the effects of high glycaemic load foods on arterial inflammation, which is an essential factor in the development of atherosclerotic plaques [32]. By contrast, low glycaemic load foods are associated with a reduced risk of cardiovascular disease, diabetes, and potentially some forms of cancer. Diets that favour low carbohydrate consumption, or foods with a low glycaemic load, generally result in greater weight loss than high carbohydrate diets. Such diets are also associated with more favourable effects on triglyceride and HDL cholesterol levels [180].

113

Vitamins and Minerals

Vitamins and minerals have various functions, and their deficiency can lead to ill-health. The common misconception is that if deficiency leads to ill-health, then consuming vast amounts will somehow improve health or improve ability to perform whatever function is associated with the nutrient. This is simply not the case. If a nutrient has a role to play in a particular function, then a deficiency may definitely prevent that function from being performed efficiently, thus some indication of malnutrition or a single nutrient deficiency may develop. However, single nutrients are not solely responsible for complicated, multistage biochemical reactions. Rather, they are at best a highly significant link in the chain. Deficiency means that the chain cannot work, but over-abundance will not have any effect on the other substances required for the reaction. If one nutrient is important for an energy reaction, then its deficiency may lead to lethargy and fatigue. Having an over-abundance of that nutrient will produce no better effects than having just enough, because a particular nutrient is simply one link in the chain. In that sense, having a link missing is a problem, and having a couple of spare links is fine, but if there are so many spare links that they start forcing their way in where they are not wanted then the consequences could be dire.

The best way to ensure that all the required nutrients are obtained through the diet is to ensure that a wide variety of fresh foods are included. Fruits and vegetables in general contain thousands of important nutrients, of which vitamins and minerals represent only the nutrients that have been most thoroughly studied and categorised. When a diet high in fruits and vegetables is associated with the prevention of a particular cancer, such as gastric cancer [5], then it is not overly important to deduce which vitamins and minerals are most abundant in the diet, because the protective substance could be any number of the thousands of other nutrients, either individually or in combination with others.

The supplementation of a particular nutrient is likely to be ineffective, because of all the other substances required for any given function. Further, by taking an abundance of one nutrient, there may be a knock-on effect, in which other nutrients are less well absorbed. Even worse, so-called mega-dosing of some nutrients has been associated with disturbances in the DNA chain, thus presenting possible risks for cancer. In short, it is best to wholly avoid supplementation of any kind, unless recommended on an individual basis by a qualified dietician or other appropriate healthcare professional. If there is a risk of a nutritional deficiency, then this should be investigated and tested for. Studies often find benefits associated with a particular nutrient, but the automatic reaction to then purchase a tablet from which to obtain that nutrient is most probably the wrong one. Nutrients are generally absorbed far better from food, and are then less likely to cause damage to the G.I. tract, or affect the absorption of other nutrients. Similarly, many studies involve the administration of nutrients intravenously, and this is because tablet forms might not allow for the absorption of the nutrient into the blood. If somebody does not have a deficiency, then there seems to be little reason to supplement nutrients. Rather, it seems wholly more sensible to enjoy a balanced diet, and if a nutrient is not included in high enough quantities, then it is the diet that should be adapted. Maintaining a sub-optimal diet and using supplements is quite possibly the least efficient, least reliable, and least cost-effective means or rectifying deficiencies.

The purpose of this section, therefore, is purely to introduce the various vitamins and minerals, along with the natural foods that represent some of the best dietary sources. This information is not intended for self-diagnosis, and the lists of foods are simply to give a general idea, and are by no means exhaustive. It is important to appreciate that foods may contain thousands of phytochemicals that are important for health, and so natural foods should be the best source of all nutrients, as opposed to supplementation, or relying on processed foods with added vitamins and minerals.

Vitamins are an inherent part of living organisms, being manufactured within plants and animals for particular processes, and passed from plant to animal, and animal-to-animal, as one eats the other. Minerals, on the other hand, originate in the soil, and are then taken up into the plants, whereby they then join the food chain in the same manner as vitamins.

115

Vitamins

Vitamin A

Vitamin A supports the immune system and may be important for the prevention of various cancers. It is involved in cell division and differentiation, fertility, and night vision. Vitamin A is also regarded as an antioxidant. Deficiency of vitamin A can lead to various skin conditions, night blindness and an increased susceptibility to infection. Excess intake can interfere with calcium and zinc absorption, and can affect metabolism of certain drugs, including corticosteroids and oral contraceptives [150,169,178].

Good Food Sources:

Apricots, asparagus, broccoli, carrots, crab, eggs, oily fish, green leafy vegetables, liver, lobster, mangoes, peaches, swordfish and tomatoes [150,169,178]. Liver is not recommended for pregnant women, due to the high concentrations of vitamin A, which can become toxic.

Vitamin C

Vitamin C is an antioxidant and is important for immune function. Vitamin C is also important for building collagen and other connective tissue (cartilage, tendons, muscle fibres, skin, etc.). It is important for tissue and capillary health, and acts as a neurotransmitter, important for the synthesis of stress hormones. Vitamin C increases iron absorption, and is important for the breakdown of cholesterol. Vitamin C is found in all living tissues. Deficiency inhibits immune function and increases susceptibility to infections. Deficiency also leads to scurvy, resulting in a lack of collagen synthesis, bleeding gums, re-opening of healed wounds, bone pain and fractures, diarrhoea and depression [150,169,178].

Good Food Sources:

Broccoli, brussels sprouts, cauliflower, peppers, green vegetables, green leafy vegetables, guava fruits, kiwi fruit, oranges, papaya, potatoes, sweet potatoes, strawberries and tomatoes [150,169,178].

Vitamin D

Vitamin D increases the absorption of calcium and is important for calcium regulation in the body. It is important for proper immune function and insulin secretion. It may be related to the prevention of some cancers, including breast cancer. Vitamin D is manufactured within the body where the skin has been exposed to sunlight, and the amount varies according to the amount of skin exposed, skin colour, age, and the intensity of sunlight (latitude, season, weather, etc.). Deficiency of vitamin D leads to rickets, osteomalacia [150,169,178]. and may have negative consequences on the musculoskeletal and immune systems, neurological function, and possibly mental health (Bishop, 2006). Rickets has been regarded as the most common non-communicable disease of childhood worldwide [18]. Low maternal vitamin D may adversely affect the development of the foetal brain. In addition to rickets, vitamin D deficiency may lead to other paediatric problems, such as hypocalcaemic fits, dental enamel hypoplasia, early-life congenital cataracts, and adverse effects on postnatal head and linear growth. The mother, both during pregnancy and lactation, requires adequate sunlight exposure and dietary intakes of vitamin D, as the infant relies on obtaining sufficient quantities from maternal supply [147].

Good Food Sources:

Eggs, liver, mushrooms, oily fish and seafood [150,169,178].

Vitamin E

Vitamin E supports the immune system and maintains the tissues of the nervous system. Vitamin E is a powerful antioxidant, and protects cell membranes from damage. It is also required for the metabolism of iron. Deficiency of vitamin E may speed the ageing process, and low intakes are associated with a high risk of cardiovascular disease [150,169,178].

Good Food Sources:

Asparagus, broccoli, green leafy vegetables, nuts, plant oils and seeds [150,169,178].

Vitamin H (Biotin)

Vitamin H is important for the metabolism of carbohydrates and fats. It is also involved in the synthesis of DNA. It is found in most living organisms and ours is manufactured in the gut. Deficiency leads to poor glucose metabolism, increased lactic acid production, lethargy, depression, hallucinations, hair loss, numbness, and skin inflammation [150,169,178].

Good Food Sources:

Cauliflower, eggs, kidneys, liver, mushrooms, nuts, peanuts, poultry, salmon and spinach [150,169,178].

119

Vitamin K

Vitamin K is important for the manufacture of blood clots, and is commonly administered to newborn babies. It is important for the formation of proteins and may be involved in bone function. The reason that it is vitamin 'K' is because the name derives from the Danish word 'koagulation', referring to its role in blood clotting. Vitamin K is manufactured in the gut, and its deficiency leads to nose bleeds, blood in the urine, stomach bleeding, minor bruising, and an inability to stop wounds from healing. The use of antibiotics can cause problems by destroying the bacteria required for manufacturing vitamin K. Vitamin E decreases vitamin K levels and its absorption [150,169,178].

Good Food Sources:

Alfalfa, asparagus, broccoli, brussels sprouts, cauliflower, green leafy vegetables, green tea, meat and liver [150,169,178].

Vitamin B$_1$ (Thiamin)

Vitamin B$_1$ is sometimes regarded as the energy vitamin, due to its role in carbohydrate metabolism and the release of energy. It is involved in a number of reactions and is important for nerve impulses. Deficiency of vitamin B$_1$ can lead to Beriberi, which affects the cardiovascular system, muscles, nerves and digestion. Deficiency can ultimately lead to severe oedema and heart failure [150,169,178].

Good Food Sources:

Asparagus, beef, eggs, figs, nuts, organ meats, peanuts, peas, pork and watermelon [150,169,178].

Vitamin B_2 (Riboflavin)

Vitamin B_2 is important for the production and liberation of energy within the body, and is involved in the metabolism of fats, carbohydrates, and other vitamins and minerals. The vitamin is important for cell formation, coenzymes, the utilisation of oxygen, and may have an antioxidant role. Deficiencies are rare, but include inflammation of the tongue, mouth and throat, cracked skin around the mouth, skin disease, and eye and nervous system disorders [150,169,178].

Good Food Sources:

Almonds, asparagus, broccoli, brussels sprouts, eggs, green vegetables, green leafy vegetables, liver, meats, and mushrooms [150,169,178].

Vitamin B_3 (Niacin)

Vitamin B_3 is important for the manufacture of fatty acids and coenzymes, for energy production, and for the metabolism and elimination of some drugs. A deficiency leads to Pellagra, resulting in widespread damage throughout the body, manifesting itself through diminished appetite, dementia, diarrhoea, dermatitis, weight loss and weakness [150,169,178].

Good Food Sources:

Almonds, asparagus, eggs, beef, fish, liver, mushrooms, peaches, potatoes and poultry [150,169,178].

121

Vitamin B$_5$ (Pantothenic Acid)

Vitamin B$_5$ is important for the production of Coenzyme A, and thereby the metabolism of carbohydrates and the production of energy. The vitamin is also involved in the production of steroid hormones. There are no known natural deficiencies in humans [150,169,178].

Good Food Sources:

Avocados, beef, broccoli, chicken, eggs, kidneys, liver, meats, mushrooms, nuts, peas, potatoes, tomatoes and seafood [150,169,178].

Vitamin B$_6$

Vitamin B$_6$ is involved in energy production and brain and nervous system function. The vitamin is involved in the regulation of water excretion, and is required by many enzymes. It is important for the formation and reactions of various amino acids, the formation of haemoglobin, and the manufacture of niacin. Vitamin B$_6$ deficiency can lead to mental health problems and convulsions. Its activity can be impaired by riboflavin and/or magnesium deficiency. The vitamin B$_6$ from meat sources can be absorbed more efficiently than that found in plant sources [150,169,178].

Good Food Sources:

Avocados, bananas, carrots, cod, eggs, fish, hazelnuts, meat, potatoes, poultry and spinach [150,169,178].

Folate

Folate (sometimes referred to as vitamin B_9) works with vitamin B_{12} and is essential for healthy red blood cells and cell division. It is therefore important for the synthesis of DNA and RNA. Deficiency leads to decreased synthesis of red blood cells, which then leads to anaemia and diarrhoea. Deficiency can be caused by a deficiency of vitamin B_{12}, and can also result from cancer therapy [150,169,178]. A deficiency may also be related to atherosclerosis, neural tube defects, adverse pregnancy outcomes, neuropsychiatric disorders, and cancer [80]. Recent research suggests that folate may be cardio-protective, although the mechanisms are not yet well understood [133].

Good Food Sources:

Asparagus, broccoli, brussels sprouts, green leafy vegetables and liver [150,169,178].

Vitamin B_{12}

Vitamin B_{12} is important for the metabolism of fatty acids and myolin, for cell division, for bone marrow and the formation of white blood cells. It is also required for the synthesis of DNA, RNA and the amino acid Leucine. As with vitamin B_6, it is absorbed best from meat sources. It works in the body with folate. Excessive intake of vitamin C can lead to a decreased bioavailability of vitamin B_{12}. Deficiency leads to folate deficiency and megaloblastic anaemia [150,169,178].

Good Food Sources:

Cod, eggs, fish, liver, meat, salmon, and seafood [150,169,178].

"If we could give every individual the right amount of nourishment and exercise, not too little and not too much, we would have found the safest way to health."

- Hippocrates

Minerals

Calcium

Calcium is the key mineral in bones and teeth. It is important for blood clotting, blood vessel and heart function, heart rate, muscle contraction, nerve function, and the storage and release of hormones. Calcium is also essential for the prevention of osteoporosis, and has also been linked with the prevention of high blood pressure. Calcium is dependent upon vitamin D and adequate oestrogen levels. Its activity determines the shape, strength and density of bone. Calcium, vitamin D, and weight-bearing exercise are essential to help prevent osteoporosis, especially in postmenopausal women, who represent the highest at-risk group. Note also that calcium and vitamin D work together to allow for increases in bone mineral density, but weight-bearing exercise is required as a stimulus for that bone formation. Men synthesise oestrogen from excess testosterone, and generally maintain sufficient hormone levels throughout life [150,169,178].

Good Food Sources:

Broccoli, green leafy vegetables (including cabbage and okra, but not spinach), fish (particularly when the bones are eaten, such as with sardines and pilchards), kelp, nuts, rhubarb and seaweed [150,169,178].

The most important factor regarding calcium and health is that of balance. Acidic foods lead to increased calcium losses, as calcium leaves the bones to return blood pH to an alkaline 7.4. Hence, whilst some foods might be high in calcium, such as dairy foods, they may actually reduce total body calcium levels by increasing calcium losses beyond any gains from the food itself.

Chromium

Chromium has been found to improve the efficiency of insulin, thereby increasing glucose uptake by cells, and hence it may be important for improved glucose tolerance. Chromium may also be involved in increasing HDL cholesterol levels. Deficiencies lead to poor glucose tolerance, with long-term deficiency possibly being associated with the onset of diabetes mellitus. Deficiencies may also be related to inappropriate blood lipid and cholesterol profiles, poor wound healing, and increased susceptibility to infection. High doses (from supplements) may be toxic in sufficient quantities. Deficiency is associated with a high intake of refined carbohydrates [150,169,178].

Good Food Sources:

Apples, asparagus, black pepper, egg yolks, meat, mushrooms, nuts, organ meats, oysters, prunes, spices and thyme [150,169,178].

Copper

Copper is an important component of the antioxidant superoxide dismutase. Copper is involved in iron absorption and metabolism. It is also involved in collagen production, blood clotting, and the protection of nerves. Copper is required for the metabolism of cholesterol, and it supports the immune system. Copper works antagonistically with molybdenum, and an increase in one leads to a decrease in the other. Deficiency of copper leads to anaemia, bone loss, and inadequate growth in developing children [150,169,178].

Good Food Sources:

Cocoa, fish, honey, non-leafy vegetables, mushrooms, nuts, organ meats, seafood, shellfish, seeds and spinach [150,169,178].

Fluoride

Fluoride protects the outer layer of teeth. It decreases the acidity of the mouth, thereby reducing the activity of the bacteria that thrive in a more acidic environment, and which in turn cause damage to the teeth. The mineral is mainly found in bones and teeth, and can replace calcium in bones if there is a calcium deficiency. Bones that use fluoride in place of calcium are not as strong as those with adequate calcium content throughout [150,169,178].

Good Food Sources:

Apples, fish, fluoridated-water, organ meats, seafood, seaweed, and tea [150,169,178].

Iodine (Iodide)

Iodine is important for the function of the thyroid gland and the regulation of metabolism. Iodine also promotes growth and development. A deficiency of iodine can lead to a decreased metabolic rate and increased serum cholesterol levels. During pregnancy, deficiency can lead to the child having mental health problems and inadequate growth. Deficiency can also lead to inflammation of the thyroid gland, which in turn leads to thyroid goiter [150,169,178].

Good Food Sources:

Plants from iodine-rich soils, saltwater fish, seafood (particularly shellfish) and seaweed [150,169,178].

Iron

Iron is required for healthy blood. Most iron (60-70%) is found in the haemoglobin of red blood cells. Iron is also involved in energy production and support of the immune system. Iron deficiency leads to anaemia. Its absorption is best from meat sources and increased vitamin C intake. Soya proteins, excessive calcium, manganese and zinc can all decrease iron absorption. Women's iron requirements increase significantly during menstruation, as iron is lost in the blood [150,169,178]. Because iron is only really lost through bleeding, it is quite rare in men. One way in which blood loss might go unnoticed (or perhaps be overlooked) is through intestinal bleeding. Chronic intestinal bleeding, as might be associated with inflammatory bowel disease (IBD), could lead to more iron being lost than is being absorbed from the diet, thus creating a deficiency [48].

Good Food Sources:
Chickpeas, egg yolks, dark leafy vegetables, liver, meats, nuts, peas, prunes, raisins, seafood, seaweed and seeds [150,169,178].

Iron supplements are commonly coated in a substance that prevents absorption. Possible side effects of iron supplementation include nausea, bloating, diarrhoea, and upper gastrointestinal pain. These are more pronounced in individuals with IBD, rather than those without it. This may, in turn, exacerbate blood loss through further damage to the gut. Furthermore, in chronic inflammatory disease the absorption of iron appears to be reduced [48].

Magnesium

Magnesium is an important mineral for maintaining bone mineral density, for enzymes, and for vitamin D activity. Magnesium is important for the regulation of substances across cell membranes. It is also important for nerve impulses and heart and lung function. A deficiency can cause an irregular heartbeat, weakness, muscle pain, seizures, and the feeling of being disorientated. Deficiency can also lead to a myocardial infarction [150,169,178].

Good Food Sources:

Broccoli, green leafy vegetables, fish, meats, nuts, seafood, seeds and spinach [150,169,178].

Manganese

Manganese is another important component of the antioxidant enzyme superoxide dismutase (as is copper). It is involved in energy production and is important for bone health. Deficiencies can lead to nausea, vomiting, poor glucose tolerance, loss of hair colour, bone loss, dizziness, hearing loss, and problems with reproductive health [150,169,178].

Good Food Sources:

Avocados, bananas, cloves, coconut, ginger, grapefruit, green vegetables, green leafy vegetables, nuts, pineapple, raspberries, seaweed and tea [150,169,178].

Molybdenum

Molybdenum is a component of the enzymes xanthine dehydrogenase and xanthine oxidase. It is involved in the metabolism of DNA, RNA, and iron, and for energy production. It helps to breakdown sulphite, and may be involved in preventing cavities. Excess molybdenum can lead to gout, via the formation of uric acid crystals that are deposited in bone joints. Molybdenum interferes with iron and copper absorption. Deficiencies lead to increased heart rate, night blindness, mental confusion, oedema, weakness, and eventually coma [150,169,178].

Good Food Sources:

Broccoli, cauliflower, dark green leafy vegetables, liver, meats, and nuts [150,169,178].

Phosphorus

Phosphorus is an important part of every body cell, essential for the formation of phospholipids, proteins and amino acids. It is essential for bone and tooth health, and for the metabolism of nutrients, including riboflavin and niacin. It is involved in the control of pH balance and excretion of waste via the kidneys. It is also a component of various enzymes and adenosine triphosphate (ATP). Phosphorus is important for healing and helps to prevent osteoporosis. It is also important for alertness and stimulating the mind. Phosphorus helps to stimulate glands to secrete hormones, and helps to maintain proper heart and muscle function. It works with calcium, and calcium cannot work effectively without adequate phosphorus. Deficiencies can lead to anxiety, poor bone health, fatigue, irregular breathing, irritability, numbness, skin sensitivity, stress, tooth weakness, tremors, general weakness, worry and changes in weight. Deficiency can also lead to malaise, stiff joints, bone pain, glucose intolerance, cardiac arrhythmia, and breathing problems. Toxicity from ingesting too much phosphorus can lead to twitching, jerking, and convulsions [150,169,178186].

Good Food Sources:

Eggs, fish, liver, meats, nuts, and poultry [150,169,178].

Potassium

Potassium is essential for the balance of fluids within the body. It is associated with decreasing blood pressure and is involved in energy metabolism and nerve impulses. Potassium is found mostly inside cells, and has a similar function to sodium. Deficiency leads to apathy, a loss of appetite, confusion, constipation, and muscle cramps. Deficiency can also cause cardiac arrhythmias, with a decreased capacity of the heart to pump blood. Low blood potassium, known as hypokalaemia, if severe can be life-threatening [150,169,178].

Good Food Sources:

Apples, asparagus, bananas, broccoli, cabbage, fish, grapefruit, meats, nuts, oranges, potatoes, poultry, seeds, shellfish and tomatoes [150,169,178].

Selenium

Selenium works with vitamin E and is a component of the enzyme glutathione peroxidase, and protects the heart and cells from oxidative damage. It may be involved in proper immune function and the prevention of cancer. Selenium is also important for the thyroid hormone and metabolism. Deficiency may lead to muscle pain, muscle wasting (atrophy), and cardiomyopathy [150,169,178].

Good Food Sources:

Broccoli, eggs, fish, garlic, meat, mushrooms, nuts, organ meats, seafood and seeds [150,169,178].

Sodium

Sodium is important for the retention and balance of water within the body. It is also involved in the absorption of nutrients, and is important for the conduction of nerve impulses. Two and a half grams of salt (half a teaspoon) contains approximately one gram of sodium. Deficiencies are not common because of the amount of salt added to foods, especially for preservation and palatability. Endurance athletes may require sodium during prolonged exercise, along with water and glucose. Symptoms of sodium deficiency include diarrhoea, muscle cramps, nausea, vomiting, potentially shock, and eventually coma [150,169,178]. Too much sodium is associated with increased blood pressure, which in turn increases the risk of heart disease, stroke and renal disease [193].

Good Food Sources:

Sodium is found naturally in low levels in all foods. It is usually found in significant quantities in diet foods, in bread, butter, cheese, margarine, bagged nuts and peanuts, milk, preserved foods, processed foods, snack foods, tinned foods and table salt [150,169,178]. Hence, it is far more likely for a person to consume too much, rather than too little sodium.

Zinc

Zinc is important for energy metabolism and for a number of enzymes. It is required for cell division, repair and growth. It is also important for DNA and RNA synthesis and function. Zinc is particularly important for reproductive health and the function of the immune system. It is required for the activation of vitamin A, and for the storage, release and function of insulin. High intakes decrease copper absorption (and therefore the activity of the antioxidant enzyme superoxide dismutase), and are associated with high LDL and low HDL cholesterol levels. Decreasing copper absorption may impact negatively on immune function. Zinc is absorbed most effectively from animal sources. Deficiency is related to poor growth rates and poor mental development in children. Deficiencies are also related to poor wound healing. Long-term deficiency can lead to skin rashes, confusion, diarrhoea, hair loss, inadequate sexual development and impaired learning ability in adolescents, a reduced appetite and skin rashes [150,169,178].

Good Food Sources:

Crab, meats, nuts, oysters, and shrimp [150,169,178].

Antioxidants and Free Radicals

A substantial body of evidence has linked free radicals and oxidative stress with various common diseases, including atherosclerosis, chronic renal failure, some cancers, diabetes mellitus, the ageing process, and various inflammatory conditions [185] including inflammatory bowel disease [165]. Oxidative stress on LDL cholesterol has been linked with the development of atherosclerotic plaques, which may in turn be responsible for cardiovascular events [185], such as heart attacks and strokes. During critical illness, too much oxidative stress can lead to multiple organ failure [1]. Furthermore, oxidative stress may affect male fertility by damaging sperm, leading to impaired conception rates, increased incidences of abortion (related to poor foetal health), and an increased incidence of infant health defects, including various genetic diseases and some childhood cancers [12].

A free radical is a molecular species capable of existing independently, and contains an unpaired electron in its atomic orbit [185]. The free radical can be considered as having either one electron too many, or one too few, and inside the body it will react with whatever is available to correct this imbalance. So, it either donates its unpaired electron to another molecule, or else it will take an electron from another molecule. This in turn causes a chain reaction, in which the affected molecule then gives or takes from another molecule, and so it goes on until the damage comes to a stop.

Free radicals are generated both within the outside environment, and within the body, as a consequence of natural reactions. Ultraviolet light, air pollutants (such as ozone and nitrogen dioxide), cigarette smoke, and various pharmaceuticals and other ingested toxins can all lead to oxidative damage [185].

Oxidative stress can be delayed or inhibited by antioxidants. Their role is therefore to prevent damage to parts of our cells that would be caused by free radicals. Antioxidants are beneficial because they interfere with the damaging chain reaction by donating electrons to the free radicals, thereby preventing further damage. The antioxidant must then be regenerated or replaced, but by its nature it does not attack other molecules. Thus, with regard to outcomes such as cardiovascular disease, increased risk could be due either to too many free radicals, a lack of antioxidants, or both [185].

Because the radicals are indiscriminate in the damage that they can cause, a range of antioxidants are required, both inside and outside the cells, to effectively defend the body. Cell membranes are made from lipids, and there are lipid antioxidants that help to defend them from damage. Vitamin E, which naturally occurs in eight different forms, is probably the most important of these. Other lipid-soluble antioxidants are the carotenoids, of which beta-carotene is considered to be the most important, but at least twenty other types may be present in cell membranes and other areas [185].

Flavonoids are a large group of antioxidants found in many fruits, vegetables, teas and wine. Over 4000 different flavonoids have been identified, and their intake has been associated with a decreased incidence of some chronic diseases, including coronary heart disease (CHD). In addition to flavonoids, other compounds found in plant foods also contribute to our overall profile of antioxidants [185]. Some flavonoids, and compounds similar to them in action, have been found to be protective against stomach ulcers and gastric adenocarcinoma [55].

As well as lipid-soluble antioxidants, there are also water-soluble antioxidants, which exist in the aqueous compartments of cells. The most important of this type of antioxidant is vitamin C, which works with a number of enzymes to limit harmful reactions within the body [185]. Some protein-based antioxidants exist in the plasma, and uric acid also scavenges free radicals [1,185].

Speculation as to which antioxidants are the most important overall, or which combinations work best, is relatively meaningless. With so many thousands of compounds with antioxidant properties, and so many ways in which they can work in combination and in different areas of the body, it is not appropriate to give specific prescriptions, especially considering that the type of damage, the area affected, the external and internal environment at the time, and the type of free radicals, all complicate the issue further [185]. The only way of knowing that someone is obtaining sufficient antioxidants, is to ensure that they are being sourced from a variety of different plant foods, rather than trying to rely on limited types of food or supplemental sources.

137

With regard to supplementation, it has been found that being administered with vitamin C can lead to increased oxidative damage, especially if iron is also administered. Furthermore, it may be that individual antioxidants do not produce effective protection from free radicals, rendering supplementation pointless and potentially harmful. The best strategy, the one that involves increasing the availability of the greatest variety of antioxidants, is the one that favours an abundance of various fruits and vegetables in the diet [185]. These foods can contain thousands of potentially beneficial phytochemicals, and there are likely to be far more benefits overall from consuming natural, nutrient-rich foods, than with reliance on basic vitamin and mineral supplements. The positive effect of fruit and vegetable intake, on improving antioxidant availability has been confirmed in both animal and human studies [61].

Bacteria

The gastrointestinal (G.I.) tract harbours more than 500 different bacterial species, many of which have important effects on health. Many of these species have evolved with us during our history, and have adapted to live and grow within us and produce beneficial health effects [56]. Some of the bacteria within our bodies are essential, to the point that we could not live without them. In effect, we exist in symbiosis with the colonies of bacteria, including those along our G.I. tract, and failure to maintain a healthy gut flora can have severe ramifications for overall health [52,56,145]. There are approximately ten times more microbial cells within the gut than there are cells in the body. Most bacteria live in the lower intestine, rather than elsewhere along the G.I. tract, due to the nature of the chemicals and various acids that exist in the stomach and upper areas of the small intestine [56].

As a society we have been as good as brainwashed into believing that bacteria are harmful. From sterilised food preparation surfaces to antibacterial handwashes, air fresheners, mouthwashes and toothpastes, we are led to believe that bacteria must be excluded from our natural home environments and from our bodies. During sickness we might be prescribed antibiotics, and there are over a thousand other pharmaceuticals that negatively affect the health of the digestive system [16]. The lower intestine harbours masses of bacteria, some of which work to prevent inflammatory bowel disease [145] and colon cancer [56].

The gut flora is important for the health of its host in many ways [2,56,145]. This includes energy production, vitamin K synthesis, immune function, maintenance of control over potentially harmful bacteria [56,145], and the absorption of calcium, magnesium and iron [56]. The bacterial colonies represent a barrier between the gut and the outside world, including against potentially harmful constituents of food that passes along the G.I. tract [145]. These 'gatekeepers' are also important for reducing stress on the liver to deal with potentially harmful toxins and so on [33].

The reported incidence of hospital deaths associated with MRSA and *Clostridium difficile* also begs certain questions. If the

139

body normally fights these conditions, might we be better off aiming for a healthy bacterial environment, rather than a sterile one? The use of antibiotics can disrupt the ecological balance within the gut, and allow overgrowth of potentially harmful bacteria. The increased prevalence of *C. difficile* has been associated with such an effect. Furthermore, once the potentially dangerous bacteria have passed through the protective barrier of the gut, they can travel around the body via the lymphatic system, entering the lymph nodes, liver and spleen. The effects of this can include sepsis, shock, multi-system organ failure, and even death [56].

Initial colonisation of the gut by microflora takes place in infancy, and matures slowly during weaning. The *improved* hygiene controls in hospitals and homes reduce early-life exposure to microbes. Effective exposure to the necessary bacteria is also managed by the normal passage of the baby out of the birth canal rather than via caesarean section [56,145].

This reduction in exposure has been associated with an increased risk of allergic diseases [75,145]. Due, in no minor part, to the extensive hygiene methods practiced in hospitals and during childbirth, children born in westernised societies have difficulty in developing an adequate gut flora [16]. Proper colonisation of bacteria is necessary for the healthy maturation of the immune system [75]. Another concern is that infants raised on an infant formula, rather than on breastmilk, have a low degree of colonisation of lactobacilli and bifidobacteria [16,56], but high counts in other bacteria, such as enterococci, coliforms, and clostridia. Excessive hygiene measures, both during childbirth and weaning, may therefore be interrupting the normal transfer of anaerobic microflora from mother to child, increasing susceptibility to allergies and infection [16].

Following the identification of microbes, bacteria were commonly regarded as a source of disease, and something that should be kept out of commercially manufactured food. Furthermore, the desire of the manufacturing industry to prolong the shelf life of their products led to steps to keep out live bacteria, coinciding with the addition of chemical additives [16].

In addition to the type of bacteria that colonise our intestines, the type of food we eat can also have profound effects on how bacteria

140

are stimulated, with potentially harmful ramifications on the host's health. Some carcinogens are formed in meat when it is cooked, and some interactions with bacteria lead to damage to DNA, whereas some bacteria can uptake and detoxify such compounds. Lactobacillus and bifidobacteria prevent the development of tumours in the colon, whereas some other bacteria (such as of the bacteroides and clostridium genera) encourage it. Having the correct bacterial environment in the gut seems to be a major factor in health and the prevention of colon cancer [56].

Our original diet would have contained several thousand times more bacteria than our contemporary diets, and a quick check to observe that we did not become extinct tells us that it could not have been harmful. Our current rising trends in disease are, however, cause for concern. Not only were our original foods higher in microbial content, but also the preservation methods were either drying, or underground storage, the latter facilitating a natural fermentation of the food [16]. As is the often the case with so many nutritional deficiencies, our answer for everything is to design a quick-fix product rather than to source the cause of a deficiency and to correct it. The initial surge of *probiotic* yoghurts onto the market presented us with a huge variety of products, the 'live bacteria' of which may have died before the product even made it onto the shelves, let alone through the various acidic environments of the human digestive system *en route* to where it might be required. Likewise, out of the hundreds of species of bacteria in our bodies, how do we know in which one or few we actually are deficient? How do we know that we will not create an imbalance and throw everything out of sync? How do we know that any dairy-based biological probiotics even survive to reach the area that we supposedly must need them?

Probiotic bacteria are the live microorganisms that stimulate the natural flora with little or no harmful effects, but with various functions of great importance to the overall health and well-being of the host, both in infancy and in adulthood [16,75]. It is becoming increasingly accepted that maintaining a healthy, probiotic environment through an adequate diet is the key to protection from potentially pathogenic microorganisms (PPMs) of bacterial, viral and fungal origin [16,56].

The World Health Organisation (WHO) has become increasingly concerned with the rising incidence of resistance to antibiotics. As a consequence, the WHO has recommended that global programmes should be introduced to reduce the use of antibiotics in our food chain, including those used to promote the growth of animals, plants and fishes [16]. The substitution of antibiotics with probiotics is producing promising findings in clinical trials [56,154]. Furthermore, the use of probiotics to treat a range of gastrointestinal diseases is gaining considerable interest [154].

Recent attention has focussed on the role of *prebiotic* carbohydrates [91]. Prebiotics are non-digestible constituents of food that selectively stimulate the growth or activity of bacterial species, in such a way as to benefit the host [56,91,165]. The beneficial effects of prebiotics are often through the metabolism in the gut of short-chain fatty acids [165]. Consumption of prebiotics is associated with the selective growth of lactobacilli and bifidobacteria, both of which are associated with positive health, and the suppression of bacteria associated with disease, such as clostridia [91,165]. Furthermore, the metabolic processes stimulate certain bacteria, which leads to the formation of metabolites that then enter the bloodstream, and are known to improve resistance to infection, improve bone quality, and reduce the risk of various chronic diseases, including cardiovascular disease and cancer. The archaeological evidence shows that prebiotics have long been a part of the human diet, and in quantities far exceeding those of many modern populations [91].

From an evolutionary perspective, the body is likely to have a natural tendency to encourage the proliferation of familiar, symbiotic, healthy bacteria, and reject those that it has not experienced in the past. Unlike in our evolutionary past, many of us are susceptible to chronic stress as a result of our contemporary lifestyles. Because misery loves company, it should be little surprise to learn that the health issues associated with stress are compounded by a knock-on affect that alters the composition of the guts' protective flora [16].

Modern populations, with a physiology and biology selected for over hundreds of thousands of years of hominin evolution, have to face the health consequences of such significant differences between our ancestral and contemporary lifestyles. The nature and composition of the modern gut microflora is therefore in discordance with that with which we evolved, and this divergence is becoming ever greater. Recent genome sequencing of *Bifidobacterium longum* has led to the finding that our two species have maintained a symbiotic and ancient relationship, coinciding with that of our own genus and the prehistoric plants that we included in our diets [91].

Acid-Base Balance

Homeostatic mechanisms operate within the body to maintain our pH at approximately 7.4 [39]. Our ancestral diets were net alkali/base yielding (high pH) because of the amounts of fruits and vegetables consumed. Conversely, the cereal and dairy foods that make up such a large proportion of our contemporary diets are net acid yielding [39,144]. Our modern diets tend to create acidic environments within our bodies, meaning that our homeostatic mechanisms are working far harder than they would have done in our distant past [144]. One potentially detrimental effect of this is that over prolonged periods of time (decades), the physiological mechanisms responsible for maintaining homeostasis may become overworked, negatively impacting on the associated metabolic pathways. This could lead to chronic calcium loss in urine, calcium loss from bones leading to dissolution, calcific urolithiasis, age-related muscle wasting, progressive deterioration of renal (kidney) function, formation of kidney stones, and kidney damage [39,144].

In making the transition from pre-agricultural hunter-gatherers to the Neolithic, some 10,000 years ago, we crossed a pH neutral zone as we went from net base to net acid production. This change was wholly due to our replacement of base-rich plant foods (fruits, vegetables and any USOs), with cereal grains, refined sugars and separated fats. These contemporary food sources do not counter the acidic effects of meats, cheeses, milk, yoghurts and eggs. Cereal grains themselves are acid-producing, and account for 38% of the acid load of all the net acid-producing foods in the contemporary diet combined [144].

In order to recover from a net acid-producing diet, we would need to remove all grain-derived food groups, including cereals, pastas, breads, refined sugars and oils, and replace them completely with unrefined, natural plant foods. Under these circumstances, animal food intake could increase considerably without it converting the diet back to a net acid-producing one [144].

If our body evolved on a net-base producing diet, then it stands to reason that our entire physiology, including the normal functioning of our organs and all other biological processes, are based on a base-producing environment. Further, it may not be simply that we are at risk of ill-health through our adoption of a net acid-producing diet, but rather that we are at risk of not realising the health benefits of a more natural, net base-producing one. A net base-producing diet could be useful in the prevention and treatment of osteoporosis, muscle wasting, calcium nephrolithiases, and sodium-chloride-sensitive hypertension. Further, this sort of diet could improve exercise performance, treat infertility, and slow the progression of age-related and disease-related chronic renal insufficiency [144].

Food Intolerances and Allergies

Food intolerances and allergies are both types of sensitivity to certain foods. The most common food intolerance in the UK is to wheat, followed by dairy products (especially cheese, yoghurt and milk), coffee, potatoes, corn, onions, beef, oats and white wine [70]. Only one of these was a significant feature of our Palaeolithic diet, and the switch from pasture to grain feeding, combined with the use of chemical and hormonal treatments has affected its composition. Food intolerances may or may not have long-term negative health consequences, and may amount to no more than decreased well-being or some unnoticeable negative affect on health.

A food allergy is an adverse immunological response to food. As such, it is not simply one single disease or caused by one simple physiological disturbance. Allergic reactions depend upon the nature of the allergy and the specific food, but can affect one or more target organs, including the skin, respiratory tract, gastrointestinal tract, and the cardiovascular system [149]. More than 70% of allergic reactions affect either the skin or G.I. tract [143,149]. Food allergies vary between childhood and adulthood. The most common food allergies in adults are milk, nuts, some fruits and vegetables and wine [143]. Children most commonly suffer allergic reactions to milk, eggs, wheat and soy [143,149].

Approximately 85% of children lose their sensitivity to most allergic foods within their first three to five years of life. By contrast, adults with food allergies can have a long-lived sensitivity, and there is now an increasingly common persistence of childhood food allergy into adulthood. This is particularly the case with sensitivity to peanuts, tree nuts, and seafood [149]. In fact, the incidence of peanut and tree nut allergy appears to be increasing [9]. Only about 20% of children younger than two years of age with a food allergy, manage to achieve tolerance by the time they reach school age [149].

There is a strong association between sensitisation to certain foods and sensitisation to pollen. Over 70% of people with a food allergy were found to have a history of hay fever. Furthermore, in the instances where food allergy occurred in conjunction with hay fever, the effects tended to be more severe [143]. There are currently no definitive recommendations regarding dietary restriction during lactation, so as to limit childhood food allergy, but the general recommendation is to breastfeed for six to twelve months, and to delay the introduction of solid foods until after the fifth month [149].

Both food allergies and intolerances are common medical problems, although there is little epidemiological data on the subject. 15.5% of the general adult population report either a food allergy or a food intolerance [143]. Proper diagnosis of a food allergy or intolerance is the key, and it is best for individuals to seek advice from an appropriately qualified healthcare professional, rather than adopting a food group restriction following self-diagnosis. When people do self-diagnose and then restrict their diet, there is the risk that they will not substitute essential nutrients and thereby cause themselves other health problems.

Water and Hydration

"I never drink water; that is the stuff that rusts pipes"
- W. C. Fields

Water is the largest single constituent of the human body [62,81,104], it is essential for the functioning of the body's cells and for life itself [62]. All reactions within the body occur in water, and water is an active participant within those reactions. Water fills virtually every space within the body, and helps to form the structures of everything within it as well [81]. Out of all of the fluids in the body, those containing the highest amount of water are the cerebrospinal fluid and bone marrow (99%), blood plasma (85%) and the brain (75%) [126]. Water is involved in digestion, absorption, transportation, and the use of nutrients, and is required for the elimination of waste and toxins [81]. It is necessary for maintaining acid-base balance, thermoregulatory balance, and hydro-electrolytic balance [126]. From the production of energy to joint lubrication to reproduction, the body requires water and there is no system within the body that does not depend upon it [81].

There has been some confusion amongst the general public with regard to how much water is actually required on a daily basis. This has partly resulted from the misinterpretation of previous recommendations, most often carried through the media by writers and/or 'experts' that did not understand the original literature [62]. Water comes from a number of sources, including fluid consumption, food content, and water metabolised from energy reactions within the body [62,104]. Fluid consumption, which represents the greatest daily constituent of water intake, can include all beverages, whether water itself or in the form of soft drinks, smoothies and, as will be shown, even coffee and alcohol. All fluids are absorbed in the gastrointestinal tract in the same manner [62].

Overall, fat-free mass in adults is approximately 70-75% water, with adipose tissue consisting of approximately 10-40% water [62]. Dehydration can have adverse affects on cognitive function, including alertness, concentration, reaction time and short-term

148

memory, and motor control including co-ordination [62,136]. A water loss amounting to a 2% drop in body weight alters thermoregulation and plasma volume. A 7% drop in hydration may cause hallucinations. 10% dehydration may cause death [126]. Early signs of dehydration include headaches, fatigue [136], loss of appetite, flushed skin, heat tolerance, light-headedness, dry mouth and eyes, a burning sensation in the stomach, and dark urine with a strong odour. As the level of dehydration increases, the signs advance to include difficulty swallowing, clumsiness, shrivelled skin, sunken eyes and dim vision, painful urination, numb skin, muscle spasms, and delirium [81].

Compensating for water loss is required to maintain health [62]. Water is lost through the urine (1500 ml/day), evaporation through the skin and lungs (900 ml/day), in faeces (100 ml/day), and through sweating. Water losses must be restored through the diet, and the total requirement is dependent upon the ambient temperature and environment, physical activity levels, type of diet, size (lean body weight in particular), and age [62,81,126].

Most people meet their daily water requirements simply by allowing their thirst to be their guide [25,62]. As a guide from the literature, the current recommendations vary from one millilitre of water per kilocalorie of energy expenditure [81,126] to a more generalised 2.7 litres of water each day for women, and 3.7 litres each day for men [25,62]. Recommendations are increased to 1.5 ml/kcal in children, and breastfeeding women should take in an additional 650-1000 ml of fluid per day [81,126]. The additional water requirement during pregnancy is to ensure that the breast milk is suitable for the baby, thus preserving the health of the mother and child [126]. Breast milk is approximately 80% water, and the average milk production during the first six months of lactation is 750 ml per day [81]. There is a slightly increased fluid requirement during pregnancy, and there is no justification for restricting fluid intake due to the inconvenience of more frequent urination [105]. Infants exclusively fed breast milk do not require any additional fluids [25].

Generally, drinking various beverages will provide 800-1500 ml of water each day [62,105,126]. Food provides between 500-1000 ml of water per day [62,105,126], with fruits and vegetables generally providing the most [81]. Dry foods, such as flours, dry pulses, uncooked pasta, and

149

so on, have between 10-15% water content. Fruits and vegetables contain approximately 90% water. How the food is cooked also affects how much water is available to the body [126]. Water is also obtained when food is metabolised in the body [62]. The calorie-containing macronutrients (lipids, carbohydrates and proteins) are broken down to release energy, with water and carbon dioxide as by-products. 100 grams of lipids produces 107 ml of water; 100 grams of carbohydrates produces 60 ml of water; and 100 grams of protein produces 40 ml of water [126]. Total daily production of water through metabolism amounts to approximately 350 ml per day, which is excluding the water content of the foods themselves [105].

Mineral water is characterised by its purity, its content of minerals, trace elements and other constituents, and its healing properties. Mineral waters can only be placed on the market after both clinical and pharmacological tests have been carried out by the Ministry of Health (for the U.K), or the equivalent body of control in other countries. The tests are to ensure that the product has all of the aforementioned qualities. Mineral waters must have favourable effects on health, be microbiologically wholesome, have a peculiar and constant chemical composition, and they must be safely bottled at their underground source. Microbiological tests of mineral waters are far stricter than those of tap water, because mineral waters cannot undergo any purification measures, and they are currently tested four times a year. The rich calcium content of some mineral waters may be particularly beneficial for those with increased requirements, such as children, pregnant women, postmenopausal women, older individuals, those with osteoporosis, and possibly others for the prevention of hypertension [126].

Many people prefer to drink mineral water rather than tap water, often due to concerns about the possible contamination of tap water by various toxic or otherwise harmful chemicals, including agricultural pesticides and industrial waste. The results of a study in Switzerland found that 80% of drinking water was significantly polluted by pesticides, and in another study, one-third of children in India were found to have a decreased short-term memory related to exposure to pesticides banned by the WHO. The safety of chlorine in drinking water has also been questioned, although the amounts found

150

in water are drastically lower than those that are obtained from food [126].

Many commonly available drinks contain caffeine [105], such as tea, coffee, hot chocolate, energy drinks, colas, and other soft drinks. As referred to in the following section, the effects of caffeine on stimulating water loss (the diuretic effect) tend to affect those that are not accustomed to consuming caffeine. Thus, there is apparently no scientific evidence to support the notion that caffeinated beverages should not excluded from the total amount of fluid consumed each day [25,105] (although there may be other reasons why some individuals should avoid caffeine). The exception to this is when caffeine consumption exceeds a moderate intake on a regular basis, which is more than two cups of coffee a day or at least six cups of tea [105]. Similarly, the diuretic effect of alcohol on fluid loss is only transient, and does not result in appreciable fluid losses over a 24-hour period [25].

During physical activity, only half the water losses are compensated for if hydration is guided by thirst alone [126]. For those that are physically active, who live in hot climates, are ill, are infants, or are elderly, thirst is a poor indicator of state of hydration [25]. These people have higher water requirements [62], and should ensure adequate hydration before, during and after activity, and throughout the day (if appropriate), both to minimise any decrease in performance and to reduce the risk of thermal stress (such as hyperthermia) [62,105].

Water requirements are also increased in all pathological conditions that involve water loss, such as diarrhoea, vomiting, hyperpyrexia, and abundant perspiration [126]. Consuming too much fluid, particularly if salt and carbohydrate content is too low, can result in hyponatraemia, which can be life-threatening [62]. This is extremely rare, usually requiring the ingestion of several litres of water within a few hours, but it was found to be the cause of death for one of the 2007 London marathon runners.

Maintaining adequate hydration is important for the prevention of kidney stones. Approximately 12-15% of the general population in the U.S. will form a kidney stone at some point in life. Of the many risk factors associated with increased risk, including age, sex, heredity, occupation, diet, social class and affluence, geographic location and climate, diet is the only one that can be easily changed.

151

Decreased fluid intake leads to a low urine volume, and increased concentrations of all stone-forming salts [81].

Dehydration over a prolonged period of time has been associated with oligohydramnios, prolonged labour, cystic fibrosis, hypertonic dehydration in infants and increased levels of toxins within the kidneys. Chronic mild dehydration may be a factor in urolithiasis, urinary tract infection, constipation, hypertension, venous thromboembolism, fatal coronary heart disease, stroke, dental disease, hyperosmolar hyperglycaemic diabetic ketoacidosis, gallstone disease, mitral valve prolapse and glaucoma [103]. Furthermore, studies have shown that there is a direct link between the amount of fluid consumed and risk of certain cancers, including urinary tract cancers, i.e., bladder, prostate, kidney, testicle), and cancers of the colon and breast. Women that consume more than five glasses of water a day were found to have a 45% decreased risk of colon cancer than women consuming two glasses or less [81]. Although accepted wisdom might be that a low water intake is associated with constipation, this is not technically the case. It is dehydration itself that is specifically linked to constipation. In other words, someone that is sufficiently hydrated, and that suffers from constipation, is not likely to receive an alleviation of their symptoms by increasing their fluid intake [136]. It is more likely that their condition will improve if they ensure that they are consuming plenty of the right types of fibre (from vegetables rather than grains), whilst avoiding foods that are potentially harmful to the gut microflora.

An individual's state of hydration is often influenced by their choice of drinks. Both adults and children tend to consume more of the sorts of things whose taste they enjoy [81,105]. In the U.S., however, beverage choice is dominated by high energy intake from sweetened drinks, including soft drinks, fruit juices, alcohol and high fat milk. These contribute a highly significant 21% of total daily energy, and all of these drinks have either low or no nutritional value whatsoever. Despite a commonly held belief that eating and drinking habits and preferences are independent, it has been shown that they are intimately linked, with those consuming less healthy foods (high-fat foods, fast foods, snacks, etc) also consuming more sweetened drinks. This suggests that these individuals are consuming calorie-rich, nutrient-poor diets, which are associated with long-term weight gain, as the body craves more food to obtain important nutrients [38]. In contrast, many people often report that drinking more fluids helps them to feel fuller and therefore to eat less [81]. It is perhaps not difficult to appreciate that those who make sensible food choices, and who favour lower-calorie drinks, will find it far easier to lose weight and to stave off hunger, than those with a poor diet.

Caffeine

Caffeine is a natural constituent of more than 60 different species of plants [88]. It is the most widely used pharmacologically active substance in the world [58,66]. Approximately 70% of the U.K. population drink tea on a regular basis, with an average daily consumption of 2.5 cups per day. Coffee is consumed by approximately 48% of the population, with an average consumption of one cup per day, however there is a wide distribution around these figures, with some individuals obviously consuming much more [105]. The average consumption of coffee in the U.S. is 200 mg [58], which roughly equates to two 220 ml (7.5 oz) cups of brewed coffee per day [88]. Significant quantities of caffeine can also be found in some soft drinks, in addition to colas, energy drinks [105], hot chocolate, chocolate, and medications [23], and is consumed by most of the population from childhood onwards [11]. The U.S. Food and Drug Administration (FDA) has listed more than 1000 over-the-counter drugs that contain caffeine [88], including cold medicines and analgesics [23].

How much caffeine is in a particular beverage varies considerably, which makes attributing accurate caffeine contents practically impossible. The caffeine content of a cup of tea, for example, will depend upon how long the tea is brewed for, whether or not the infusion is stirred, the leaf to water ratio, and the size of the serving [105]. In addition, the type of tea leaves used and the various processing techniques and procedures undergone prior to the tea reaching the shelves can be significant [23].

Caffeine is completely absorbed through the gastrointestinal tract, and reaches peak blood concentrations within thirty to sixty minutes. It has a half-life of approximately four to six hours, meaning that this is the amount of time for caffeine levels in the blood to halve. Total blood caffeine levels will therefore be increased by subsequent caffeine ingestion during the day [88]. The half-life of caffeine is doubled by the use of oral contraceptives, and is increased with pregnancy [11] and hormone treatments [10]. People generally consume the most caffeine at times when they feel lethargic, such as shortly after waking or following a meal, particularly after lunch [23].

Caffeine may improve mood and increase alertness. This effect is most apparent in low arousal situations, such as upon waking or following a meal [11,151]. It has been shown to increase vigilance and improve attention span in individuals that become lethargic following meals [88]. In doses that would normally be obtained through normal drinking habits, caffeine has been found to reduce reaction times and improve performance during vigilance tasks, and in other tasks that benefit from a high level of alertness [66,151]. Greater effects are associated with higher doses [66]. Although high doses of caffeine can increase the time that it takes someone to fall asleep, this is not necessarily the case with people that consume a low-to-moderate amount of caffeine before bed, and there is no clear evidence to suggest that the affects are significant enough to negatively affect health and well-being. Because most people can manage their own intakes quite effectively, there is no strong evidence relating caffeine consumption with sleeping problems [151].

Caffeine is able to penetrate the protective blood-brain barrier, and thereby directly influence the central nervous system [11,88]. Further, caffeine has been reported to reduce blood flow to the brain, and a sudden withdrawal of caffeine can lead to headaches that are alleviated by resuming caffeine consumption. It is suggested that the withdrawal causes blood vessels to dilate, thus causing a headache [11].

Coffee consumption is associated with increases in serum cholesterol levels, with greater amounts of coffee having a greater affect [88]. However, this effect is unique to boiled coffee, and is not due to caffeine itself. As boiling coffee is unusual in many westernised countries, most consumers are not at risk [11,88]. Caffeine has, however, been shown to raise both systolic and diastolic blood pressure, and people with higher blood pressures already, are affected to a greater extent than those with normal or optimal levels [58]. Further, caffeine has been associated with cancers of the bladder, kidneys, ovaries, pancreas, and breast. However, the associations are reportedly weak, and the carcinogenic effect is not likely to be manifested in an individual until after many years of use [88]. However, such an implication of association does warrant some caution whilst we await the findings of further studies.

Caffeine is a stimulant of the kidneys, and can increase fluid loss through increased urination [88]. This diuretic effect is overcome in habitual caffeine users, and tends only to affect individuals consuming over 250 mg of caffeine a day (roughly equivalent to two cups of filter coffee) [105]. Caffeine also stimulates respiratory function, increasing blood flow, ventilation rate and depth. Caffeine has therefore been used effectively to treat asthmatics [88].

Regular caffeine users become habituated to the effects of caffeine. The effects become reduced in individuals that are accustomed to consuming caffeinated products on a regular basis [105]. Many studies that have reported adverse effects of caffeine use have assessed people that have abstained from caffeine consumption for a set period prior to testing, and/or were administered with unusually high caffeine doses that they, as individuals, were not accustomed to. For those that do regularly consume caffeinated drinks, it does not increase urine output or negatively affect hydration status [25].

For pregnant women it is important to be aware that caffeine freely crosses the placenta, with plasma caffeine concentrations in the neonate being similar to those in the mother. It may therefore be appropriate to limit caffeine intake during pregnancy, at least keeping to a moderate intake of two cups of coffee a day or less (less than 300 mg of caffeine). Intakes above this have been associated with decreased birthweight (which can lead to adverse health consequences later in life) and in some cases miscarriage [105].

Caffeine intake has been linked with increased urinary and faecal calcium losses. This coincides with other reports of caffeine stimulating calcium losses from bones. These factors could have huge significance for those at risk for osteoporosis, in which low bone mineral content is associated with an increased risk of fractures, and is highly prevalent in elderly women. The relationship between caffeine consumption and total fracture risk tends to be most prevalent in those that consume the greatest amount of caffeine (equivalent to more than six cups of coffee per day). Those at risk from osteoporosis may therefore benefit from reducing their caffeine intake, if required [57].

100 mg of caffeine, roughly equivalent to that found in two cups of tea or less than one cup of coffee, has been found to increase metabolic rate by 3-4% over two and half hours. At doses of 300-500

mg of caffeine, basal metabolic rate (BMR) is elevated by approximately 10%, and this effect can last up to four hours. These results have been shown to increase energy expenditure, and this thermogenic effect may be enhanced with physical activity [88]. Whilst this may have some benefits for weight loss, it is not recommended for those with cardiovascular risk factors, including those for hypertension and/or atherosclerosis.

Moderate caffeine intakes may have the positive effect of reducing the risk of Parkinson's disease. In men the effect is linear, with greater intake being associated with a reduced risk. In women the association is U-shaped, meaning that moderate caffeine intake (roughly equivalent to one to three cups of coffee per day) appears to be better than either abstaining completely or consuming too much. These positive effects were attributable to caffeine itself, from coffee, tea and other caffeinated beverages, and not to decaffeinated coffee [10].

Negative effects of too much caffeine consumption include anxiety [151], diuresis, diarrhoea, insomnia, withdrawal headaches, heartburn, tremors, nausea, irritability, and even cardiac arrhythmias [11,88,148]. A morning dose of two to three cups of coffee produces a large effect on blood pressure, with the greatest negative effect being on those with hypertension [58]. In extreme cases even death has been reported as the result of acute caffeine poisoning [88]. Children are also at risk from the behavioural effects of caffeine, and some children consume surprisingly large amounts [11].

Whilst too much caffeine will produce problems, for the majority of the population that only consumes moderate amounts, it is unlikely to cause any short-term negative effects. Indeed, the positive effects of caffeine on alertness and vigilance may be of particular benefit to health and safety in certain workplace and other environments [151]. In those with optimal or normal blood pressures, moderate caffeine intake does not elevate blood pressure beyond normal values [58]. Those that are particularly sensitive to its effects should avoid caffeine, in particular those with panic disorders. The effects of caffeine may also exacerbate schizophrenic and manic-depressive symptoms [11]. Caffeine-containing plants may well have constituted a part of the diets of our Palaeolithic ancestors, although consumption would have been significantly less than the concentrations currently available in drinks and medication. The association between caffeine and osteoporosis and various cancers requires further investigation.

Alcohol

"Alcohol is necessary for a man so that he can have a good opinion of himself, undisturbed by the facts"

- Finley Peter Dunne

The association between light to moderate drinking and better health has become quite robust, despite the specific causality not always being particularly clear. The benefits of light to moderate drinking are associated with cardiovascular health, and specifically to the apparent cardio-protective effects of ethanol [28]. These benefits occur for intakes of less than two drinks per day in men [140] and an average of less than one per day for women [28]. Because cardiovascular diseases represent such a common cause of premature death in westernised populations, the benefits of alcohol consumption are suggested to outweigh the risks (which include death from liver cirrhosis, injury, haemorrhagic stroke, breast cancer, and perhaps large bowel cancer) [28].

The problem with many of the studies is that they do not accurately assess the effects of diet. For example, many assess saturated fat intake, but certainly not all factors related to health. There is some evidence that light to moderate drinkers generally have a healthier diet in any case. Wine drinkers have been found to live longer than abstainers, but because the studies did not appropriately assess diet, it is likely that other factors could have been responsible. Wine tends to be consumed preferentially by people in higher social classes, and a higher social class in general is associated with light to moderate drinking. In some studies, there are simply not enough variables that are considered, and the apparently protective effect of alcohol disappears when exercise and obesity are taken into account [28].

With regard to osteoporosis, there a number of mechanisms by which alcohol consumption may be related to an increased risk of fractures. These include abnormal properties of bone, reduced rates of bone formation, and reduced active areas

159

available for building new bone. Alcohol may also have a direct toxic effect on bone [57], as well as encouraging calcium losses through its presence in the blood. Additionally, alcohol is not recommended if there is evidence of organ damage that could be linked to alcohol, or if there is a past or family history of alcohol dependence or harmful drinking. Alcohol is also not recommended during pregnancy, [28]. In fact, alcohol has been found to be causally linked to more than 60 different medical conditions, and detrimentally so in most cases. The risks include various cancers, neuropsychiatric disorders, cardiovascular disorders, gastrointestinal diseases, and intentional and unintentional injuries. The exceptions to the negative effects of alcohol on well-being relate to cardiovascular health, especially coronary heart disease (CHD), stroke and diabetes mellitus [140]. With regards to these conditions, there is some evidence that alcohol may have beneficial and/or protective effects, although more extensive research is still required.

For most diseases, the risk is directly related to the volume of alcohol consumed. In general though, it is not only the total weekly alcohol consumption that predicts negative consequences on health, but also heavy drinking on an irregular basis [140]. Excessive alcohol consumption is the primary diet-related risk factor for liver cancer in Western countries [78]. Episodic heavy drinking (binge drinking) is associated with an increased risk for major coronary events, including strokes and sudden cardiac death. This link is consistent with increased blood clotting, a lowered threshold for ventricular fibrillation, and elevation of LDL cholesterol [140]. Heavy drinking is associated with deaths from liver disease, various cancers, and various cardiovascular diseases, including strokes [49].

There is a linear association between average alcohol consumption and risk of breast cancer. Oestrogen replacement therapy after the menopause also increases the risk of breast cancer, and when combined with alcohol consumption the risk is significantly magnified [140]. The margin of safety for alcohol consumption is therefore narrower for women than for men, due to the association of breast cancer deaths with consuming more than two or three drinks per day [28].

Over the coming years, more research should focus on investigating the association of alcohol with overall health, and not only those factors which apply to certain 'at-risk' groups (such as heart disease, for which the most at-risk group is middle-aged, overweight men). Doctors have been rightly blamed for sometimes recommending alcohol for relieving stress or to help someone to sleep, which may in turn lead to alcohol dependence [28]. The association between light to moderate alcohol consumption and health is almost entirely due to the positive effects of ethanol on cardiovascular health, which is the reverse of what occurs with heavy drinking. Beyond that, there is some scepticism that the benefits found in the studies relate to alcohol consumption at all, and are not simply related to status (and hence the improved diet and physical activity habits associated with it). The development of some cancers is associated with alcohol consumption in general, and it may be that as the prevalence of less common cancers becomes more apparent, the positive aspects of alcohol consumption may be offset [49]. As more evidence comes to light, it can be expected that more appropriate guidelines will be developed for when alcohol should be recommended, if at all.

In light of the available information, it is neither necessarily appropriate to consider alcohol as a protective strategy against disease, nor as a particularly unhealthy behaviour [49]. Light to moderate alcohol intake is generally associated with better dietary habits in any case. If the result of both light to moderate drinking and a healthy diet demonstrate a marked positive effect on health, then we have to ask if promoting alcohol consumption is focusing on the correct factor out of the two. Alcohol may have both positive and negative consequences, whereas a healthy diet on its own has only positives. Put another way, if someone does not consume alcohol and has a less than optimal diet, are we right to follow the recommendations that suggest increasing alcohol intake as the *best* positive step?

With a diet that is already very high in fruits and vegetables, the body will be better able to deal with the potentially harmful effects of alcohol intake, and so a healthy diet should be the first goal. Alcohol was not a large feature in our Palaeolithic pasts, save for the consumption of some foods that were partially fermented during

161

preservation. Therefore, with alcohol not being a part of the natural diet, and not necessarily conferring the health benefits often touted by the media, it remains that alcohol should be consumed for reasons other than any proposed nutritional benefits for health. Alcohol does offer distinct and pleasurable flavours, as well as promoting a reduction in stress, with a light to moderate intake permitting these whilst offering the least negative affects on health. Validation beyond that cannot be offered in a text based on our ancestral diet.

Food Additives

A food additive is any substance that is added to food, which is not commonly regarded as food itself. They are usually added to affect how long the food lasts, its texture, consistency, taste, colour, acidity or alkalinity, or for any other technological function, including processing. Food additives generally belong to one of three main groups; cosmetics, preservatives, or processing aids. In a review of food additives published in 1994, it was reported that there were close to 4000 food additives in use, of which 3640 were purely used for cosmetic purposes, some being used as processing aids, and a mere 2% purely for food preservation [168]. The use of food additives has increased dramatically over the past thirty years, with over 200,000 tonnes of food additives being produced each year.

A study of the Finnish population reported that most of the food additive intakes were well below the acceptable daily intakes, as suggested by the World Health Organisation (WHO). There were a number of additives, however, which were consumed in sufficient quantities to warrant cause for concern. These included nitrates, nitrites, saccharin, cyclamates, SAIB and benomyl [123].

Some considerable scientific data has linked intolerance to food additives with various physical and mental disorders, including childhood hyperactivity. A further issue is that the addition of chemicals can reduce the nutritional content of foods, so much so that many foods and drinks now have added vitamins and minerals, thus missing out on the vast gamut of other beneficial phytochemicals, which were lost and subsequently not replaced. If the mainstay of the diet is these foods with a low nutritional value, then it may be far easier to gain weight as the body craves more and more food in the hope of obtaining necessary nutrients. In the meantime the individual may be suffering from sub-clinical malnutrition. The addition of sucrose in place of naturally occurring carbohydrates is a good case in point. Natural sources of carbohydrate are primarily of plant origin, either fruit or vegetable, and contain thousands of phytochemicals, including essential and protective vitamins and minerals. Sucrose, by definition, contains literally no nutrients and only calories [123].

163

Aspartame (also known as NutraSweet or E951 [158]) is an artificial sweetener used in more than 6000 diet products, beverages, and pharmaceuticals [108]. Aspartame was first approved in France in 1979, and subsequently in the U.K. in 1983 [158]. It is approximately 180-200 times sweeter than sugar [158]. A study on rodents in 2006, gave us the first compelling evidence that aspartame is carcinogenic through a number of mechanisms. Most importantly, its carcinogenic effects can be realised at an intake equivalent to half of the maximum safe dose for Europeans (20 mg per kilogram of bodyweight against maximum recommendations of 40 mg per kilogram of bodyweight in Europeans, and 50 mg per kilogram in Americans) [152]. The results of this study were then confirmed and reinforced by a further study, published in 2007, which showed that the carcinogenic effect of aspartame is increased if exposure begins during foetal life [153]. Cancer risk was found to increase directly with the intake of aspartame [108]. The greatest carcinogenic effects corresponded with an intake of 100 mg of aspartame per kg of bodyweight, which is equivalent to a 20.4 kg (45 lb or 3 stone, 3 lb) child drinking five cans of a diet soft drink [108].

There are currently more than 200 million people that regularly consume aspartame, including women of child-bearing age and children. If the U.S. FDA were to conclude that the findings of the two studies were correct, and that aspartame does indeed cause cancer, then they would be required by law to revoke its approval for the additive [108]. Likewise, the Food Standards Agency in the U.K. has stated its intention to continue to monitor the relationship between aspartame and health [158].

Other chemical additives have also been linked with cancer development, including curcumin (E100), carmoisine (E122), amaranth (E123), ponceau (E124), erythrosine (E127), Brown FK, sulphites (E210-E219), nitrates and nitrites (E249-E252), butylated hydroxyanisole (E320), monosodium glutamate (MSG), and saccharin. The potentially negative effects of any one of these chemicals, especially as they are taken in such minute quantities, are not really likely to cause any serious harm. The problem, however, is that some people consume diets containing so many additive-containing foods, and it is the combination of so many chemical additives interacting with each other, and within us, that poses the greatest risk [168]. It may take many years, or many decades, before such effects become noticeable, and consequently it is a difficult area for the development of scientifically *proven* safe upper limits.

The consumption of food additives has been associated with a number of negative health consequences, including (but most probably not limited to) eczema, urticaria, angioedema, exfoliative dermatitis, irritable bowel syndrome, nausea, vomiting, diarrhoea, rhinitis, bronchospasm, migraine, anaphylaxis, hyperactivity and other behavioural disorders. An inappropriate diet can have profound negative effects on physical, mental and behavioural health. Between 1985 and 1990 there was a 42% rise in the number of children under 10 years of age being seen by psychiatric services, a 65% increase in children between 10 and 14, and a 21% increase in 15 to 19 year olds. Nowadays there are children as young as five being admitted to psychiatric wards. Although nutritional problems may not be the sole cause of these health problems, it may at least represent a contributory factor. A first step in the treatment of any child being admitted to a psychiatric ward should surely include an assessment for chemical or other dietary intolerance [168].

Diet can also have long-term effects on reproductive health, and the future health of the infant, as maternal health can be a factor in predicting a successful pregnancy and the child's future health. Even sub-clinical malnutrition can lead to a reduction in foetal brain development, potentially leading to various intellectual deficits. There is now no doubt that for a child to be born healthy and mentally and physically undamaged, all necessary dietary changes should be made by both parents, well in advance of conception. This is to help ensure that both the ova and the sperm are undamaged [168].

Despite the government and media pinning the rising trend in criminal statistics on various socio-political influences (TV, film and computer game violence, poverty, lack of parental guidance, alleged child abuse, frustration, lack of motivation, lack of appropriate prisons or institutions, police and so on and so forth), it seems that everything has been blamed except inappropriate nutrition [168]. Yet we know that nutrition affects brain development and behaviour, from influences that affect an individual well in advance of their birth. Whilst it might

165

be fanciful to assume that nutrition is the only factor responsible, it seems equally foolish to assume that it could not be involved in anything less than a significant part. This is particularly the case when it is considered in conjunction with socio-political factors.

Whilst this section has been heavily influenced by a particularly compelling review by Tuormaa (1994) [168], there is one final point that author makes that I believe to be of particular importance. The present treatment for childhood hyperactivity includes a range of psychotropic drugs. Should it be the case that hyperactivity is due to exposure to harmful chemicals, either with or without a nutritionally insufficient diet, then a treatment that involves administering more chemicals is questionable. One such chemical compound is Ritalin, and the author of the article regards its administration to hyperactive children as bordering on the barbaric. The reason for this is that Ritalin has such devastating side effects, including growth depression, dyskenisias and tics, hallucinations and delusional disorders, seizures, headaches, blurred vision, "zombie-like" behaviour and hair loss. The withdrawal symptoms include severe and prolonged depression and suicide [168]. The point is not so much to advise against medical treatments, but rather to emphasise the worthiness of investigating nutritional factors first. If eight weeks of conversion onto an additive-free, natural diet can improve behaviour, then this may represent a long-term and drug-free solution to be explored.

Ideally, governments should take a stronger stance on controlling food additives, and more should be done to educate people about the possible health consequences of consuming a variety of chemicals throughout life.

The Secret of our Evolutionary Success

Our success as a species is the result of adaptation, invention and innovation over the course of more than three million years. During this time, we became ever more reliant on animal foods than on the plant foods that sustained our more distant ancestors [91,94,112,156]. We became dietary generalists [63,181], whilst our primate cousins began fitting into niches as specialists [181]. This marked a deviation of our ancestors to a new means of subsistence, which coincided with a greater dependence on tools and upon the role of individuals within communities, with food sharing and so on [132]. Men became the hunters and/or scavengers, whilst women and juveniles became gatherers [39]. It appears likely that our success as a species was due to the variety of important roles played by all individuals within a community.

What followed from our new generalist strategy was a greater dietary breadth, quality and stability than ever before. These dietary and behavioural adaptations facilitated the development of larger brains, an anatomically different digestive system to other apes, and the cultures and tool uses that define our populations today [94]. All of these factors developed together; tool use and problem solving, which combined with meat eating permitted larger brains. As the processing and greater reliance on meat allowed for a smaller gut, so it used less energy which in turn allowed more to be used by our ever more energy-demanding brains [91,134]. The importance of being energy efficient in how we moved when hunting and gathering also improved our upright walking posture, thus giving us a favourable ratio of energy used in obtaining food, to energy derived from that food [93]. These were clearly not single events, but continued to develop throughout most of human history, defining us as species. This multifaceted development of our genus helps to explain why our australopithecine ancestors, who persisted for over 1.5 million years after adopting an upright walking posture, did so without developing much larger brains. Their fate was sealed with the coming ice age and shrinking forests, as they were not as specialised as other tree-dwelling primates, and unable to compete with us on the grasslands [157].

Our requirement for a great number of essential nutrients to maintain our health and well-being, goes back several million years. If we can be described as unique as a species, then it is through our diverse diet and ability to optimise what is available through technology, initiative and innovation [91]. When the climatic changes affected the African habitats, our ape cousins became specialist frugivores, whilst our ancestors stepped forth and found ways of encompassing all available high-quality food resources into their diets [119]. We became the greatest global innovators of all the mammals, a trend that continues to this day. The greatest challenge for us, is to marry this understanding of our place in nature, with the acceptance of the conflict between our genotype and our lifestyles. In the application of this, we hold the key to preventing and/or treating modern disease and obesity, both for ourselves as individuals, and for the global population as a whole.

Conclusions

"Inherently, each one of us has the substance within to achieve whatever our goals and dreams define. What is missing from each of us is the training, education, knowledge and insight to utilize what we already have."

- Mark Twain

In the United States, chronic illnesses and other health problems, either partially or wholly attributable to diet, represent by far the most serious threat to public health [32]. A number of researchers have concluded that humans are maladapted to diets of domesticated and processed plant foods as these foods are recent in evolutionary timescales, and consequently a number of doctors and nutritionists are starting to advocate a Palaeolithic (pre-agricultural) diet [134]. Throughout more than 99 percent of our history, humans evolved on a diet that was void of dairy foods, margarine (separated fats), cultivated cereal grains, and refined sugars, the combination of which supply as much as 60 to 70% of the calories in many modern diets [60,91].

The key to a healthy diet is variety. We require about fifty *essential* nutrients for proper growth, metabolic function and cellular repair [91]. Lean meat, leafy green vegetables and fruits are advisable as health-promoting foods, because they are the foods on which our distant human ancestors thrived. By contrast, dairy products, cereals, beans, separated fats, refined carbohydrates and added salt, are all new and have occurred too recently for our genome to have adapted to them [97]. Evidence is growing that these contemporary foods are having negative consequences on our health, especially with regard to the modern prevalence of chronic diseases [97,107]. Furthermore, cooking, burning and smoking foods produces high levels of potentially harmful molecules, many of which have an affect on our DNA and are carcinogens [29].

Many of the chronic diseases that afflict westernised populations are the result of our contemporary diets, our lifestyles and our environment. Consequently, we can see that reverting to a

169

Palaeolithic approach would be likely to remove, or at least significantly limit, such diseases from modern society. In fact, the entire concept of a *natural* diet is often ridiculed as being over simplistic [39]. The reason for this dashing of our potential salvation is quite straightforward. The diets that we chose to adopt in Africa, within the last three million years, are quite different from those of our later ancestors living in other parts of the world. We know, for example, that our earliest human diet would have been similar to that of the australopithecines, with our greater inclusion of animal foods being the only difference. Two million years ago, the diets of our ancestors would have been even more firmly based around the exploitation of animal foods. By the time Palaeolithic humans and our contemporaries reached northern Europe and the sub-Arctic, our diets were almost, if not entirely, animal-based. As mankind left Africa and migrated across the globe, different regions would have presented different varieties of plant and animal species, in addition to the availability of seafood.

Unlike today, in each region our ancestors would have thrived on a variety of thousands of different species, taken from hundreds of genera of plant foods, much of which may have become seasonally-available in less equatorial latitudes. How are we to prescribe a diet based on so many variations and so many unknowns? More to the point, why does it matter? With regard to the ratio of animal to plant foods, we should probably refer to the ratio of our African ancestors of about two million years ago. This represents a ratio of animal to plant foods of 65:35. Although our diets changed and adapted following our migration out of Africa, most of these changes were behavioural and cultural, relying on tools and different means of preparing food for consumption. Our genome was founded, adapted, and evolved in the opening savannahs of Africa, and that is where we should look to base a more definitive Palaeolithic, or natural, diet.

Secondly, does it really matter which specific fruits and vegetables we consumed? The reason for this question is that we are, in any case, bound to eat only what is available to us. That is, regardless of what we might have been eating during the last two million years, we are now restricted to what we can buy and what we can grow.

With this in mind, the concept of adopting *our* natural diet is absurd and unrealistic. We do not know exactly what it was and we could not procure everything in it even if we wanted to. However, what we do know is what it was like. We know that it was high in wild animal meat, often comprising up to two-thirds of our ancestral diet [107], but it was not just the animal's muscle tissue. When we obtained a carcass we would have eaten the organs, the bone marrow and the brain. Significantly, we would have eaten those out of preference to the muscle tissue. We ate from a variety of wild plant foods, including thousands of different types of fruits and vegetables [29].

Modern diets contain less meat and more total fat and carbohydrate (the latter coming from very few plant sources; predominantly refined grain), in addition to increasing amounts of refined sugar [107]. Whilst further investigation is necessary, especially with human subjects, the Palaeolithic lifestyle presents the most robust dietary strategy than any other proposed health-promoting diet today [97].

The fundamental principle of human health and optimal nutrition is that a diverse diet, comprised of a variety of natural foods, increases overall health patterns by lowering infant mortality rates and increasing life expectancy. Finally, for those concerned with fat loss, for whom energy deficiency will need to take place for the diet to be effective, having a balanced diet with the full breadth of essential nutrients is the key [60]. Once a diet is healthy, then calorie-restriction can take place without placing additional stress on the body to source sufficient nutrients from foods, and consequently this may help predict the long-term success of a calorie-restricted diet.

A growing trend over the last few years has been the growth and diversity within the 'functional foods' market. One way of viewing this could be from the perspective that adding inadequate additives to a poor diet is not the ideal solution. It is, however, typical of our contemporary lifestyles that consumer demand exists for such products. The philosophy of this book is that diets are less healthy because they are less natural. Therefore, I would struggle to find

171

adequate support for the argument that adding individual unnatural products to an already poor-quality contemporary diet is really the answer. This latter approach appears to give us the potential to have the worst of both worlds [52].

Replacing an inadequate contemporary diet with a more natural one would appear to give us the opportunity to obtain the best of what there is available, and therefore it wins on the grounds of pure logic, before even considering anything else. Our genotype evolved when we were exploiting generalist eating strategies, and including ever more wild meats into our diets. As a species we will not thrive if we selfishly expect all of our shortcomings in health to be compensated for by global leaps in technology and medicine. Nor can we expect our species to evolve defences to the current onslaught within the next few generations.

Finally, it would be unfair to suppose that a change in dietary behaviour was the only important factor in modern disease and ill-health. Environmental stress, such as from noise and pollutants, are also damaging, as is psychological stress. These issues have not been dealt with in this book because it is outside of the research that was incorporated, and each would need a book of its own to be produced to give them fair appraisal. In defence, however, a healthy diet and lifestyle are known to help protect the body against the effects of psychological and environmental stress.

The key to mental and physical health, including the prevention and treatment of disease, lies in seeking ways of marrying the diets of our Palaeolithic ancestors, with the natural foods that we have available today. Thus, on an individual level we may be able to enjoy the benefits of better health, whilst as a global species we have the potential to reduce modern disease, and hopefully to allow for the balance of funding to shift in favour of research and treatment into the cases for which diet is less effectual. In other words, by reducing and better controlling incidences of heart disease and cancer, for example, less would need to be spent on treatment overall, and funds could be made available for more targeted research, as well as providing the potential pools of funding for other important healthcare issues, such as combating HIV and AIDS, Alzheimer's and Parkinson's disease, and managing better hygiene in hospitals.

172

"Western society has accepted as unquestionable a technological imperative that is quite as arbitrary as the most primitive taboo: not merely the duty to foster invention and constantly to create technological novelties, but equally the duty to surrender to these novelties unconditionally, just because they are offered, without respect to their human consequences."

- Lewis Mumford

Appendices

Appendix I

References

References

1.   Abiles, J. S., "Oxidative stress is increased in critically ill patients according to antioxidant vitamins intake, independently of severity: a cohort study", Critical Care, 2006, 10, R146

2.   Agarwal, P. K., "Enzymes: An integrated view of structure, dynamics and function", Microbial Cell Factories, 2006, 5, 2

3.   Aggett, P. J., "Symposium on 'Trace elements and human health'", Proceedings of the Nutrition Society, 1988, 47, 21-25

4.   Aiello, L. C., Wheeler, P., "On diet, energy metabolism, and brain size in human evolution", (Reply), Current Anthropology, 1996, 37 (1), 128-129

5.   Allum, W. H., Griffin, S. M., Watson, A., Colin-Jones, D., "Guidelines for the management of oesophageal and gastric cancer", Gut, 2002, 50 (Supplement V), v1-v23

6.   Anderson, A. S., "The Pro Children study – a cross-national approach to increasing fruits and vegetables in the next generation and onwards", International Journal of Behavioural Nutrition and Physical Activity, 2006, 3, 26

7.   Antón, S. C., "Natural history of Homo erectus", Yearbook of Physical Anthropology, 2003, 46, 126-170

8.   Arasaradnam, R. P., Riley, S. A., Corfe, B. M., "Diet and colorectal cancer: fibre back on the menu?" Gut, 2004, 24, 155-156

9.   Armstrong, D., Rylance, G., "Definitive diagnosis of nut allergy", Archives of Disease in Childhood, 1999, 80, 175-177

10.   Ascherio, A., Zhang, S. M., Hernán, M. A., Kawachi, I., Colditz, G. A., Speizer, F. E., Willett, W. C., "Prospective study of caffeine consumption and risk of Parkinson's disease in men and women", Annals of Neurology, 2001, 50, 56-63

11.   Ashton, C. H., "Caffeine and health", British Medical Journal, 1987, 295 (6609) 1293-1294

12.   Baker, M. A., Aitken, R. J., "Reactive oxygen species in spermatozoa: methods for monitoring and significance for the origins of genetic disease and infertility", Reproductive Biology and Endocrinology, 2005, 3: 67

13. Bartolli, R., Fernández-Bañares, F., Navarro, E., Castellà, Mañé, J., Alvarez, M., Pastor, C., Cabré, E., Gassull, M. A., "Effect of olive oil on early and late events of colon carcinogenesis in rats: modulation of arachidonic acid metabolism and local prostaglandin E_2 synthesis", Gut, 2000, 46, 191-199

14. Baumer, J. H., "Obesity and overweight: Its prevention, identification, assessment and management", Archives of Diseases in Childhood, 2007, 92, 92-96

15. Benefit, B. R., McCrossin, M. L., "Miocene Hominoids and Hominid origins", Annual Review of Anthropology, 1995, 24, 237-256

16. Bengmark, S., Ecological control of the gastrointestinal tract. The role of probiotic flora", Gut, 1998, 42, 2-7

17. Biggee, B. A., Blinn, C. M., McAlindon, T. E., Nuite, M., Silbert, J. E., "Low levels of human serum glucosamine after ingestion of glucosamine sulphate relative to capability for peripheral effectiveness", Annals of Rheumatic Diseases, 2006, 65, 222-226

18. Bishop, N., "Don't ignore vitamin D", Archives of Disease in Childhood, 2006, 91, 549-550

19. Blumenberg, B., Todd, N. B., (Reply), Current Anthropology, 1975, 16 (3), 466

20. Boaz, N. T., Hampel, J., "Strontium content of fossil tooth enamel and diet of early hominids", Journal of Paleontology, 1978, 52 (4), 928-933

21. Bocherens, H., Drucker, D. G., Billiou, D., Patau-Mathis, M., Vandermeersch, B., "Isotopic evidence for diet and subsistence pattern of the Saint-Césaire I Neanderthal: review and use of a mulit-source mixing model", Journal of Human Evolution, 2005, 49, 71-87

22. Booth, F. W., Chakravarthy, M. V., Spangenberg, E. E., "Exercise and gene expression: physiological regulation of the human genome through physical activity", Journal of Physiology, 2002, 543 (2), 399-411

23. Brice, C. F., Smith, A. P., "Factors associated with caffeine consumption", International Journal of Food Sciences and Nutrition, 2002, 53, 55-64

177

24.   Broadhurst, C. L., Cunnane, S. C., Crawford, M. A., "Rift Valley lake fish and shellfish provided brain-specific nutrition for early Homo", British Journal of Nutrition, 1998, 79 (1), 3-21

25.   Campbell, S. M., "Hydration needs throughout the lifespan", Journal of the American College of Nutrition, 2007, 26 (5), 585S-587S

26.   Carlson, B. A., Kingston, J. D., "Docosahexaenoic acid, the aquatic diet, and hominin encephalisation: Difficulties in establishing evolutionary links", American Journal of Human Biology, 2007, 19, 132-141

27.   Cavadini, C., Sierga-Riz, A. M., Popkin, B. M., "US adolescent food intake trends from 1965 to 1996", Archives of Disease in Childhood, 2000, 83, 18-24

28.   Chick, J., "Alcohol, health, and the heart: Implications for clinicians", Alcohol and Alcoholism, 1998, 33 (6), 576-591

29.   Coffey, D. S., "Similarities of prostate and breast cancer: Evolution, diet, and estrogens", Urology, 2001, 57 (Supplement 4A), 31-38

30.   Conference Review, "Food, nutrition, and the prevention of cancer: A global perspective", Nutrition, 1999, 15 (6), 523-526

31.   Cordain, I., Eaton, S. B., Miller, Brand Miller, J., Mann, N., Hill, K., "The paradoxical nature of hunter-gatherer diets: meat-based, yet non-atherogenic", European Journal of Clinical Nutrition, 2002, 56 (Supplement 1), S42-S52

32.   Cordain, L., Eaton, S. B., Sebastian, A., Mann, N., Lindeberg, S., Watkins, B. A., O'Keefe, J. H., Brand-Miller, J., "Origins and evolution of the Western diet: health implications for the 21st century", American Journal of Clinical Nutrition, 2005, 81, 341-354

33.   Dietrich, C. G., Geier, A., Oude Elferink, R. P. J., "ABC of oral bioavailability: Transporters as gatekeepers in the gut", Gut, 2003, 52, 1788-1795

34.   Dietrich, C. G., Geier, A., Wasmuth, H. E., de Waart, D. R., Oude Elferink, R. P. J., Matern, S., Gartung, C., "Influence of biliary cirrhosis on the detoxification and elimination of a food derived carcinogen", Gut, 2004, 53, 1850-1855

35.	Dobzhansky, T., "On the Evolutionary Uniqueness of Man", Evolutionary Biology, 1972, 6, 415-430

36.	Dray, X., Boutron-Ruault, M-C., Bertrais, S., Sapinho, D., Benhamiche-Bouvier, A-N., Faivre, J., "Influence of dietary factors on colorectal cancer survival", Gut, 2003, 52, 868-873

37.	Druce, M., Bloom, S. R., "The regulation of appetite", Archives of Disease in Childhood, 2006, 91, 183-187

38.	Duffey, K. J., Popkin, B. M., "Adults with healthier dietary patterns have healthier beverage patterns", The Journal of Nutrition, 2006, 136, 2901-2907

39.	Eaton, S. B., "The ancestral human diet: what was it and should it be a paradigm for contemporary nutrition?", Proceedings of the Nutrition Society, 2006, 65, 1-6

40.	Eaton, S. B., Eaton, S. B., "Evolution, diet and health", 1998, Departments of Anthropology and Radiology, Emory University, Atlanta, Georgia, USA. Poster: www.cast.uark.edu/local/icaes/conferences/wburg/posters/sboydeaton/eaton.htm

41.	Feher, M. D., "Lipid lowering to delay the progression of coronary artery disease", Heart, 2003, 89, 451-452

42.	Feinman, R. D., "When is a high fat diet not a high fat diet?", Nutrition and Metabolism, 2005, 2 (27)

43.	Forster, S., Gariballa, S., "Age as a determinant of nutritional status: A cross sectional study", Nutrition Journal, 2005, 4, 28

44.	Frayn, K. N., Coppack, S. W., Potts, J. L., "Effect of diet on human adipose tissue metabolism", Proceedings of the Nutrition Society, 1992, 51, 409-418

45.	Fredriks, A. M., van Buuren, S., Wit, J. M., Verloove-Vanhorick, S. P., "Body index measurements in 1996-7 compared with 1980", Archives of Disease in Childhood, 2000, 82, 107-112

46.	Frezza, E. E., Wachtel, M. S., Chiriva-Internati, M., "Influence of obesity on the risk of developing colon cancer", Gut, 2006, 55, 285-291

47.	Galgani, J., Aguirre, C. Diaz, E., "Acute effect of meal glycemic index and glycemic load on blood glucose and insulin responses in humans", Nutrition Journal, 2006, 5 (22)

48.   Gasche, C., Lomer, M. C. E., Cavill, I., Weiss, G., "Iron, anaemia, and inflammatory bowel diseases", Gut, 2004, 53, 1190-1197

49.   Gaziano, J. M., Gaziano, T. A., Glynn, R. J., Sesso, H. D., Ajani, U. A., Stampfer, M. J., Manson, J. E., Hennekens, C. H., Buring, J. E., "Light-to-moderate alcohol consumption and mortality in the Physicians' Health Study enrolment cohort", Journal of the American College of Cardiology, 2000, 35 (1), 96-105

50.   Ghaneh, P., Costello, E., Neoptolemos, J. P., "Biology and management of pancreatic cancer", Gut, 2007, 56, 1134-1152

51.   Giovannucci, E., Stampfer, M. J., Colditz, G. A., et al, "Multivitamin use, folate, and colon cancer in women in the Nurse's Health Study, Annals of Internal Medicine, 1998, 129, 517-514

52.   Goodlad, R. A., "Dietary fibre and the risk of colorectal cancer", Gut, 2001, 48, 587-589

53.   Gough, A., Sheeran, T., Bacon, P., Emery, P., "Dietary advice in systemic sclerosis: the dangers of a high fibre diet", Annals of Rheumatic Disease, 1998, 57, 641-642

54.   Grayson, D. K., Delpech, F., "Changing diet breadth in the early upper Palaeolithic of southwestern France", Journal of Archaeological Science, 1998, 25, 1119-1129

55.   Graziani, G., D'Argenio, G., Tuccillo, C., Loguercio, C., Ritieni, A., Morisco, F., Del Vecchio Blanco, C., Fogliano, V., Romano, M., "Apple polyphenol extracts prevent damage to human gastric epithelial cells in vitro and to rat gastric mucosa in vivo", Gut, 2005, 54, 193-200

56.   Guarner, F., Malagelada, J-R., "Gut flora in health and disease", The Lancet, 2003, 360 (8), 512-519

57.   Hansen, S. A., Folsom, A. R., Kushi, L. H., Sellers, T. A., "Association of fractures with caffeine and alcohol in postmenopausal women: the Iowa Women's Health Study", Public Health Nutrition, 2000, 3 (3), 253-261

58.   Hartley, T. R., Sung, B. H., Pincomb, G. A., Whitsett, T. L., Wilson, M. F., Lovallo, W. R., "Hypertension risk status and

effect of caffeine on blood pressure", Hypertension, 2000, 36, 137-141

59.   Hayes, M., Chustek, M., Heshka, S., Wang, Z., Pietrobelli, A., Heymsfield, S. B., "Low physical activity levels of modern Homo sapiens among free-ranging mammals", International Journal of Obesity, 2005, 29, 151-156

60.   Hockett, B., Haws, J., "Nutritional ecology and diachronic trends in Palaeolithic diet and health", Evolutionary Anthropology, 2003, 12, 211-216

61.   Hoensch, H., Morgenstern, I., Petereit, G., Siepmann, M., Peters, W. H. M., Roelofs, H. M. J., Kirch, W., "Influence of clinical factors, diet, and drugs on the human upper gastrointestinal glutathione system", Gut, 2002, 50, 235-240

62.   Institute of Medicine, (2004) "Dietary Reference Intakes for water, potassium, sodium, chloride and sulphate" National Academies Press, Washington D. C., United States.

63.   Isaac, G., "The diet of early man: aspects of archaeological evidence from lower and middle Pleistocene sites in Africa", World Archaeology, 1971, 2 (3), 278-299

64.   Ismail, J., Jafar, T. H., Jafary, F. H., White, F., Faruqui, A. M., Chaturvedi, N., "Risk factors for non-fatal myocardial infarction in young South Asian adults", Heart, 2004, 90, 259-263

65.   Janssen, M. A., Sept, J. M., Griffith, C. S., "Foraging of *Homo ergaster* and *Australopithecus boisei* in East African environments", Proceedings of the Annual Conference of the North American Association of Computation Social and Organisational Science, 2005, June 26-28, 1-6

66.   Jarvis, M. J., "Does caffeine intake enhance absolute levels of cognitive performance?", Psychopharmacology, 1993, 110, 45-52

67.   Jeffery, R. W., Baxter, J. E., McGuire, M. T., Linde, J. A., "Are fast food restaurants an environmental risk factor for obesity?" International Journal of Behavioural Nutrition and Physical Activity, 2006, 3, 2

68.   Jian, L., Zhang, D. H., Lee, A. H., Binns, C. W., "Do preserved foods increase prostate cancer risk?", British Journal of Cancer, 2004, 90, 1792-1795

69.   Jin, H., Hwang, S-K., Yu, K., Anderson, H. K., Lee, Y-S., Lee, K. H., Prats, A-C., Morello, D., Beck Jr, G. R., Cho, M-H., "A high inorganic phosphate diet perturbs brain growth, alters Akt-ERK signalling, and results in changes in cap-dependent translation", Toxicological Sciences, 2006, 90 (1), 221-229.

70.   Jones, J., Boorman, J., Cann, P., Forbes, A., Gomborone, J., Heaton, K., Hungin, P., Kumar, D., Libby, G., Spiller, R., Read, N., Silk, D., Whorwell, P., "British society of gastroenterology guidelines for the management of irritable bowel syndrome", Gut, 2000, 47, (Supplement II), ii1-ii19

71.   Jönsson, T., Ahrén, B., Pacini, G., Sundler, F., Wierup, N., Steen, S., Sjöberg, T., Ugander, M., Frostegård, J., Göransson, L., Lindeberg, S., "A Palaeolithic diet confers higher insulin sensitivity, lower C-reactive protein and lower blood pressure than a cereal-based diet in domestic pigs", Nutrition and Metabolism, 2006, 3, 39

72.   Jordinson, M., El-Hariry, I., Calnan, D., Calam, J., Pignatelli, M., "*Vicia faba* agglutinin, the lectin present in broad beans, stimulates differentiation of undifferentiated colon cancer cells", Gut, 1999, 44, 709-714

73.   Jowett, S. L., Seal, C. J., Pearce, M. S., Phillips, E., Gregory, W., Barton, J. R., Welfare, M. R., "Influence of dietary factors on the clinical course of ulcerative colitis: a prospective cohort study", Gut, 2004, 53, 1479-1484

74.   Jurmain, R., "Degenerative joint disease in African great apes: an evolutionary perspective", Journal of Human Evolution, 2000, 39 (2), 185-203

75.   Kalliomäki, M., Salminen, S., Poussa, T., Arvilommi, H., Isolauri, E., "Probiotics and prevention of atopic disease: 4-year follow-up of a randomised placebo-controlled trial", Lancet, 2003, 361, 1869-1871

76.   Kaplan, H., Hill, K., Lancaster, J., Magdalena Hurtado, A., "A theory of human life history evolution: diet, intelligence, and longevity", Evolutionary Anthropology, 2000, 9, 156-185

77.   Kelley, J. R., Duggan, J. M., "Gastric cancer epidemiology and risk factors", Journal of Clinical Epidemiology, 2003, 56, 1-9

78.   Key, T. J., Schatzkin, A., Willett, W. C., Allen, N. E.,
        Spencer, E. A., Travis, R. C., "Diet, nutrition and prevention of
        cancer", Public Health Nutrition, 2004, 7 (1A), 187-200
79.   Khaw, K-T., "Epidemiology of coronary heart disease in
        women", Heart, 2006, 92 (Supple III), iii2-iii4
80.   Kim, Y-I., "Folate: a magic bullet or a double edged sword
        for colorectal cancer prevention?", Gut, 2006, 55, 1387-1389
81.   Kleiner, S. M., "Water: An essential but overlooked
        nutrient", Journal of the American Dietetic Association, 1999, 99
        (2), 200-206
82.   Knekt, P., Järvinen, R., Dich, J., Hakulinen, T., "Risk of
        colorectal and other gastro-intestinal cancers after exposure to
        nitrate, nitrite, and N-nitroso compounds: A follow-up study",
        International Journal of Cancer, 1999, 80, 852-856
83.   Kopelman, P. G., Grace, C., "New thoughts on managing
        obesity", Gut, 2004, 53, 1044-1053
84.   Krantz, G. S., "Brain size and hunting ability in earliest
        man", Current Anthropology, 1968, 9 (5), 450-451
85.   Labayen, I., Forga, L., González, A., Lenoir-Wijnkoop, I.,
        Nutr, R., Martínez, J. A., "Relationship between lactose digestion,
        gastrointestinal transit time and symptoms in lactose
        malabsorbers after dairy consumption", Alimentary
        Pharmacology and Therapeutics, 2001, 15, 543-549
86.   Labib, M., "The investigation and management of obesity",
        Journal of Clinical Pathology, 2003, 56, 17-25
87.   Lagergren, J., "Adenocarcinoma of oesophagus: what exactly
        is the size of the problem and who is at risk?" Gut, 2005, 54
        (Supplement I), i1-i5
88.   Lamarine, R. J., "Selected health and behavioural effects
        related to the use of caffeine", Journal of Community Health,
        1994, 19 (6), 449-466
89.   Laugesen, M., Elliot, R., "Ischaemic heart disease, Type 1
        diabetes, and cow milk A1 β-casein", The New Zealand Medical
        Journal, 2003, 116 (1168), 295-309
90.   Leach, J. D., "Evolutionary perspective on dietary intake of
        fibre and colorectal cancer", European Journal of Clinical
        Nutrition, 2007, 61, 140-142

91.   Leach, J. D., Gibson, G. R., Van Loo, J., "Human evolution, nutritional ecology and prebiotics in ancient diet", Bioscience Microflora, 2006, 25 (1), 1-8

92.   Leonard, W. R., Robertson, M. L., "Evolutionary perspectives on human nutrition: The influence of brain and body size on diet and metabolism", American Journal of Human Biology, 2005, 6 (1), 77-88

93.   Leonard, W. R., Robertson, M. L., "On diet, energy metabolism, and brain size in human evolution", (Discussion and Criticism), Current Anthropology, 1996, 37 (1), 125-129

94.   Leonard, W.R., Snodgrass, J.J., Robertson, M. L., "Effects of brain evolution on human nutrition and metabolism", Annual Review of Nutrition, 2007, 27, 311-327

95.   Levi, F., Lucchini, F., Negri, E., La Vecchia, C., "Trends in mortality from cardiovascular and cerebrovascular diseases in Europe and other areas of the world", Heart, 2002, 88, 119-124

96.   Lindeberg, S., "Palaeolithic diet ("stone age" diet)", Scandinavian Journal of Nutrition, 2005, 49 (2), 75-77

97.   Lindeberg, S., Cordain, L., Boyd Eaton, S., "Biological and clinical potential of a Palaeolithic diet", Journal of Nutritional and Environmental Medicine, 2003, 13 (3), 149-160

98.   Little, J., "Multivitamins, folate, and colon cancer", Gut, 2001, 48, 12-13

99.   Macho, G. A., Spears, I. R., "Effects of loading on the biomechanical behaviour molars of Homo, Pan, and Pongo", American Journal of Physical Anthropology, 109, 211-227

100.   Macko, S. A., Engel, M. H., Andrusevich, V., Lubec, G., O'Connell, T. C., Hedges, R. E. M., "Documenting the diet in ancient human populations through stable isotope analysis of hair", Philosophical Transactions of the Royal Society, 1999, 354, 65-76

101.   Macko, S. A., Lubec, G., Teschler-Nicola, M., Andrusevich, V., Engel, M. H., "The Ice Man's diet as reflected by the stable nitrogen and carbon isotopic composition if his hair", FASEB, 1999 (a), 13, 559-562

102.   Mann, J. I., Appleby, P. N., Key, T. J., Thorogood, M.,
        "Dietary determinants of ischaemic heart disease in health
        conscious individuals", Heart, 1997, 78, 450-455
103.   Manz, F., "Hydration and disease", Journal of the American
        College of Nutrition, 2007, 26 (5), 535S-541S
104.   Manz, F., Wentz, A., "24-h hydration status: parameters,
        epidemiology and recommendations", European Journal of
        Clinical Nutrition, 2003, 57 (Supplement 2), S10-S18
105.   Maughan, R. J., Griffin, J., "Caffeine ingestion and fluid
        balance: a review", Journal of Human Nutrition and Dietetics,
        2003, 16, 411-420
106.   McGuire, M. A., McGuire, M. K., "Conjugated linoleic acid
        (CLA): A ruminant fatty acid with beneficial effects on human
        health", Journal of Animal Science, 2000, 77, 1-8
107.   McMichael, A. J., "Integrating nutrition with ecology:
        balancing the health of humans and biosphere", Public Health
        Nutrition, 2005, 8 (6A), 706-715
108.   Mead, M. N., "Aspartame cancer risks revisited",
        Environmental Health Perspectives, 2007, 115 (9), A460
109.   Menzies, I. S., Zuckerman, M. J., Nukajam, W. S.,
        Somasundaram, Murphy, B., Jenkins, A. P., Crane, R. S.,
        Gregory, G. G., "Geography of intestinal permeability and
        absorption", Gut, 1999, 44, 483-489
110.   Mieres, J. H., "Review of the American Heart Association's
        guidelines for cardiovascular disease prevention in women",
        Heart, 2006, 92 (Supplement III), iii10-iii13.
111.   Millward, J. D., "Optimal intakes of protein in the human
        diet", Proceedings of the Nutrition Society, 1999, 58, 403-413
112.   Milton, K., "Animal source foods to improve micronutrient
        nutrition and human function in developing countries: The
        critical role played by animal source foods in human (Homo)
        evolution", The Journal of Nutrition, 2003, 133, 3886S-3892S
113.   Milton, K., "Nutritional characteristic of wild primate foods:
        Do the diets of our closest living relatives have lessons for us?",
        Nutrition, 1999, 15 (6), 488-498

185

114.   Moazzez, R., Anggiansah, A., Botha, A. J., Bartlett, D., "Association of achalasia and dental erosion", Gut, 2005, 54, 1665-1666

115.   Muskiet, F. A. J., Fokkema, R., Schaafsma, A., Rudy Boersma, E., Crawford, M. A., "Is docosahexaenoic acid (DHA) essential? Lessons from DHA status regulation, our ancient diet, epidemiology and randomised controlled trials", Journal of Nutrition, 2004, 134, 183-186

116.   Nagao, M., Sugimura, T., "Carcinogenic factors in food with relevance to colon cancer development", Mutation Research, 1993, 290, 43-51

117.   Noakes, M., Foster, P. R., Keogh, J. B., James, A. P., Mamo, J. C., Clifton, P. M., "Comparison of isocaloric very low carbohydrate/high saturated fat and high carbohydrate/low saturated fat diets on body composition and cardiovascular risk", Nutrition and Metabolism, 2006, 3 (7)

118.   Norat, T., Riboli, E., "Dairy products and colorectal cancer. A review of possible mechanisms and epidemiological evidence", European Journal of Clinical Nutrition, 2003, 57, 1-17

119.   O'Connell, J. F., Hawkes, K., Blurton Jones, N. G., "Grandmothering and the evolution of Homo erectus", Journal of Human Evolution, 1999, 36, 461-485

120.   Oates, J. F., "Water-plant and soil composition by Guereza Monkeys (Colobus guereza): a relationship with minerals and toxins in the diet?", Biotropica, 1978, 10 (4), 241-253

121.   Paramsothy, P., Knopp, R., "Management of Dyslipidaemias", Heart, 2006, 92, 1529-1534

122.   Paulionis, L., Kane, S-L., Meckling, K. A., "Vitamin status and cognitive function in a long-term care population", BMC Geriatrics, 2005, 5 (6)

123.   Penttilä, P-L., Salminen, S., Niemi, E., "Estimates on the intake of food additives in Finland", Zeitschrift fur Lebensmitteluntersuchung und –Forschung A, 1988, 186, 11-15

124.   Pérez-Pérez, A., Bermúdez De Castro J. M., Arsuaga, J. L., "Nonocclusal dental microwear analysis of 300,000-year-old Homo heidelbergensis teeth from Sima de los Huesos (Sierra de

Atapuerca, Spain)", American Journal of Physical Anthropology, 1999, 108, 433-457

125.   Peters, C. R., O'Brien, E. M., "The early hominid plant-food niche: Insights from an analysis of plant exploitation by Homo, Pan, and Papio in Eastern and Southern Africa", Current Anthropology, 1981, 22 (2), 127-140

126.   Petraccia, L., Liberati, G., Masciullo, S. G., Grassi, M., Fraioli, A., "Water, mineral waters and health", Clinical Nutrition, 2006, 25, 377-385

127.   Poppitt, S. D., Kilmartin, P., Butler, P., Keogh, G. F., "Assessment of erythrocyte phospholipid fatty acid composition as a biomarker for dietary MUFA, PUFA or saturated fatty acid intake in a controlled cross-over intervention trial", Lipids in Health and Disease, 2005, 4, 30

128.   Poulter, N., "Global risk of cardiovascular disease", Heart, 2003, 89 (Supplement II), ii2-ii5

129.   Povey, A. C., Hall, C. N. Hall, Badawi, A. F., Cooper, D. P., O'Conner, P. J., "Elevated levels of the pro-carcingenic adduct, O^6-methylguanine, in normal DNA from the cancer prone regions of the large bowel", Gut, 2000, 47, 362-365

130.   Prentice, A. M., Moore, S. E., "Early programming of adult diseases in resource poor countries", Archives of Disease in Childhood, 2005, 90, 429-432.

131.   Puente, X. S., Velasco, G., Gutiérrez-Fernández, A., Bertranpetit, J., King, M-C., López-Otín, C., "Comparative analysis of cancer genes in the human and chimpanzee genomes", BMC Genomics, 2006, 7 (1): 15

132.   Ragir, S., "Diet and food preparation: Rethinking early hominid behaviour", Evolutionary Anthropology, 2000, 9 (4), 153-155

133.   Reddy, K. S., Katan, M. B., "Diet, nutrition and the prevention of hypertension and cardiovascular diseases", Public Health Nutrition, 2004, 7 (1A), 167-186

134.   Richards, M. P., "A brief review of the archaeological evidence for Palaeolithic and Neolithic subsistence", European Journal of Clinical Nutrition, 2002, 56

187

135.   Richards, M. P., Pettitt, P. B., Trinkaus, E., Smith, F. H., Paunović, M., Karavanić, I., "Neanderthal diet at Vindija and Neanderthal predation: The evidence from stable isotopes", PNAS, 2000, 97 (13), 7663-7666

136.   Ritz, P., Berrut, G., "The importance of good hydration for day-to-day health", Nutrition Reviews, 2005, 63 (6) (II) S6-S13

137.   Roder, D. M., "The epidemiology of gastric cancer", Gastric Cancer, 2002 (Supplement 1), 5-11

138.   Roediger, W. E. W., Babidge, W., "Human colonocyte detoxification", Gut, 1997, 41, 731-734

139.   Romero, A., De Juan, J., "Scanning microscopy exam of hominoid dental enamel surface: Exploring the effect of abrasives in the diet", http://www.formatex.org/microscopy2/papers/1-17.pdf

140.   Room, R., Babor, T., Rehm, J., "Alcohol and public health", The Lancet, 2005, 365, 519-530

141.   Rosiński, F., Kasprowicza, A. J., "On the idea of association between Homo and Australopithecus", Current Anthropology, 1975, 16 (3), 465-466

142.   Savaiano, D. A., Levitt, M. D., "Milk intolerance and microbe-containing dairy foods", Journal of Dairy Science, 1987, 70 (2), 397-406

143.   Schäfer, T., Böhler, E., Ruhdorfer, S., Weigl, L., Wessner, D., Heinrich, J., Filipiak, B., Wichmann, H.-E., Ring, J., "Epidemiology of food allergy/food intolerance in adults: associations with other manifestations of atopy", Allergy, 2001, 56, 1172-1179

144.   Sebastian, A., Frassetto, L. A., Sellmeyer, D. E., Merriam, R. L., Curtis Morris Jr, R., "Estimation of the net acid load of the diet of ancestral preagricultural Homo sapiens and their hominid ancestors", American Journal of Clinical Nutrition, 2002, 76, 1308-1316

145.   Segal, I., Walker, A. R. P., Wadee, A., "Persistent low prevalence of Western digestive diseases in Africa: confounding aetiological factors", Gut, 2001, 48, 730-732

146.   Sharkey, D., Gardner, D., Sebert, S., Bos, P., Symonds, M., Budge, H., "Unique juvenile obesity model and the crucial role of

inflammation", Archives of Disease in Childhood, 2007, 92 (Suppl I): A26-A30

147.   Shaw, N. J., Pal, B. R., "Vitamin D deficiency in UK Asian families: activating a new concern", Archives of Disease in Childhood, 2002, 86, 147-149

148.   Shirlow, M. J., Mathers, C. D., "A study of caffeine consumption and symptoms: Indigestion, palpitations, tremor, headache and insomnia", International Journal of Epidemiology, 1985, 14, 239-248

149.   Sicherer, S. H., "Food Allergy", The Lancet, 2002, 360, 701-710

150.   Silverman, H., M., Romano, J., Elmer, G., (1999) "The Vitamin Book", Bantam Books, London, United Kingdom

151.   Smith, A., "Effects of caffeine on human behaviour", Food and Chemical Toxicology, 2002, 40, 1243-1255

152.   Soffritti, M., Belpoggi, F., Esposti, D. D., Lambertini, L., Tibaldi, E., Rigano, A., "First experimental demonstration of the multipotential carcinogenic effects of aspartame administered in the feed to Sprague-Dawley rats", Environmental Health Perspectives, 2006, 114 (3), 379-385

153.   Soffritti, M., Belpoggi, F., Tibaldi, E., Esposti, D. D., Lauriola, M., "Life-span exposure to low doses of aspartame beginning during prenatal life increases cancer effects in rats", Environmental Health Perspectives, 2007, 115 (9), 1293-1297

154.   Spiller, R., (a) "Nutritional Influences on survival from colorectal cancer", Gut, 2003, 52 (6), 775

155.   Spiller, R., "Can probiotics enhance mucosal defence?", Gut, 2003, 52 (6), 775.

156.   Sponheimer, M., Lee-Thorp, J. A., "Isotopic evidence for the diet of an early hominid, Australopithecus africanus", Science, 1999, 283, 368-370

157.   Stanley, S. M., "An ecological theory for the origin of Homo", Paleobiology, 1992, 18 (3), 237-257

158.   Stanner, S. A., "Aspartame in the news again", British Nutrition Foundation, 2005, 30, 309-310

159.   Stewart, L., van de Ven, L. N. M., Jackson, P., Reilly, J. J., Wilson, D. C., "Confirmation of the high prevalence of paediatric

obesity in children and teenagers with special needs and refutation of the hypothesis that this could be explained by socio-economic status", Archives of Disease in Childhood, 2007, 92 (Suppl I): A26-A30

160.   Swagerty, D. L., Walling, A. D., Klein, R. M., "Lactose Intolerance", American Family Physician, 2002, 65, 1845-1850, 1855-1856

161.   Tashiro, M., Akiyama, T., Yoshikawa, I., Kume, K., Otsuki, M., "Obesity as a risk factor for colorectal polyps in Japanese patients", Gut, 2004, 24, 156

162.   Tavani, A., Bosetti, C., Augustin, L. S., Jenkins, D. J. A., La Vecchia, C., "Carbohydrates, dietary glycaemic load and glycaemic index, and risk of acute myocardial infarction", Heart, 2003, 89, 722-726

163.   Teaford, M. F., Ungar, P. S., "Diet and the evolution of the earliest human ancestors", PNAS, 2000, 97 (25), 13506-135111

164.   Thorgeirsoon, U. P., Dalgard, D. W., Reeves, J., Adamson, R. H., "Tumor incidence in a chemical carcinogensis study of nonhuman primates", Regulatory Toxicology and Pharmacology, 1994, 19, 130-151

165.   Tilg, H., Kaser, A., "Diet and relapsing ulcerative colitis: take off the meat?", Gut, 2004, 53, 1399-1401

166.   Tinahones, F. J., C-Soriguer, F. J., Collantes, E., Perez-Lindon, G., Sanchez Guijo, P., Lillo, J. A., "Decreased triglyceride levels with low calorie diet and increased renal excretion of uric acid in hyperuricaemic-hyperlipidaemic patients", Annals of the Rheumatic Diseases, 1995, 54 (7), 609

167.   Tsugane, S., "Salt, salted food intake, and risk of gastric cancer: Epidemiologic evidence", Cancer Sci. 2005, 96 (1), 1-6

168.   Tuormaa, T. E., "The adverse effects of food additives on health: A review of the literature with special emphasis on childhood hyperactivity", Journal of Orthomolecular Medicine, 1994, 9 (4), 225-243

169.   Ulene, A., (1997) "The NutriBase Complete Book of Food Counts (The NutriBase Nutrition Centre Series)", Avery Publishing Group Inc. United States.

170.   Ungar, P. S., Grine, F. E., Teaford, M. F., Zaatari, S. E., "Dental microwear and diets of African early Homo", Journal of Human Evolution, 2006. 50. 78-95

171.   Ungar, P., "Dental topography and diets of Australopithecus afarensis and early Homo", Journal of Human Evolution, 2004, 46, 605-622

172.   Van der Auwera, I., Wera, S., Van Leuven, F., Henderson, S. T., "A ketogenic diet reduces amyloid beta 40 and 42 in a mouse model of Alzheimer's disease", Nutrition and Metabolism, 2005, 2, 28

173.   Van Uffelen, J. G. Z., Hopman-Rock, M., Chin A Paw, M. J. M., Van Mechelen, W., "Protocol for Project FACT: a randomised controlled trial on the effect of a walking programme and vitamin B supplementation on the rate of cognitive decline and psychosocial wellbeing in older adults with mild cognitive impairment", BMC Geriatrics, 2005, 5 (18)

174.   Verhaegen, M., Munro, S., "Australopiths wading? Homo diving?", Symposium: Water and Human Evolution, 1999, University Gent, Flanders, Belgium Proceedings, http://www.radicalanthropologygroup.org/class_text_013.doc

175.   Wakai, K., Ohno, Y., Genka, K., Ohmine, K., Kawamura, T., Tamakoshi, A., Lin, Y., Nakayama, T., Aoki, K., Fukuma, S., "Risk modification in lung cancer by a dietary intake of preserved foods and soyfoods: findings from a case-control study in Okinawa, Japan", Lung Cancer, 1999, 25, 147-159

176.   Wang, D., DuBois, R. N., "Prostaglandins and cancer", Gut, 2006, 55, 115-122

177.   Ward, M. H., Pan, W-H., Cheng, Y-J., Li, F-H., Brinton, L. A., Chen, C-J., Hsu, M-M., Chen, I-H., Levine, P. H., Yang, C-S., Hildesheim, A., "Dietary exposure to nitrite and nitrosamines and risk of nasopharyngeal carcinoma in Taiwan", International Journal of Cancer, 2000, 86, 603-609

178.   Wardlaw, G. M., Insel, P. M., (1996) "Perspectives in Nutrition", Third Edition, Mosby, London, United Kingdom

179.   Whiting, S. J., Barabash, W. A., "Dietary Reference Intakes for the micronutrients: considerations for physical activity", Applied Physiology, Nutrition and Metabolism, 2006, 31, 80-85

180.	Wolever, T. M. S., Gibbs, A. L., Spolar, M., Hitchner, E. V., Heimowitz, C., "Equivalent glycaemic load (EGL): a method of quantifying the glycaemic responses elicited by low carbohydate foods", Nutrition and Metabolism, 2006, 3 (33)

181.	Wood, B., Strait, D., "Patterns of resource use in early *Homo* and *Paranthropus*", Journal of Human Evolution, 2004, 46, 119-162

182.	Wood, D., Wray, R., Poulter, N., Williams, B., Kirby, M., Patel, V., Durrington, P., Reckless, J., Davis, M., Sivers, F., Potter, J., "JBS 2: Joint British Societies' guidelines on prevention of cardiovascular disease in clinical practice", Heart, 2005, 91 (Supplement V), v1-v52

183.	Woolf, A. D., Breedveld, F. C., Kvien, T. K., "Controlling the obesity epidemic is important for maintaining musculoskeletal health", Annals of Rheumatic Disease, 2006, 65, 1401-1402

184.	Ye, W., Lagergren, J., Weiderpass, E., Nyrén, O., Adami, H-O., Ekbom, A., "Alcohol abuse and the risk of pancreatic cancer", Gut, 2002, 51, 236-239

185.	Young, I. S., Woodside, J. V., "Antioxidants in health and disease", Journal of Clinical Pathology, 2001, 54, 176-186

186.	http://www.vitamins-nutrition.org/vitamins/phosphorus.html

187.	http://www.weightlossresources.co.uk/diet/gi_diet/glycaemic_index_tables.htm

188.	http://www.mendosa.com/gilists.htm

189.	http://www.hsph.harvard.edu/nutritionsource/carbohydrates.html

190.	http://www.nutritiondata.com/topics/glycemic-index

191.	http://www.medicinenet.com/your_cholesterol_profile_-_in_depth/article.htm

192.	http://anthropology.si.edu/HumanOrigins/ha/erec.html

193.	http://www.epha.org/a/1912

Appendix II

Glossary

Glossary

Acanthosis nigricans - a skin disorder characterised by velvety, light-brown-to-black markings on the skin

Acheulean Industry - Refers to particular style of stone tools in use between 1.5 million and 200,000 years ago. Named after the archaeological site Saint-Acheul, in northern France. Such tools are associated with *Homo erectus* and early *Homo sapiens*

Acne vulgaris ('common acne') - Most people experience acne as teenagers as the result of changes in hormones (androgens and oestrogens)

Adenoma – Benign growths of glandular origin that can cause health problems by compressing other structures

Anaemia – condition characterised by abnormally low haematocrit and haemoglobin levels. This is associated with a decreased capacity for blood to carry oxygen, and can lead to unusual tiredness, lethargy, palpitations, headaches, sore mouth and gums, and brittle nails

Analgesics – Group of drugs used to achieve analgesia, or 'painkilling'

Anaphylaxis – severe (potentially fatal) allergic multi-organ (systemic) reaction

Angioedema – severe local swelling of skin

Antioxidant – any substance that limits oxidative damage

Arboreal – relating to or resembling a tree/living in a tree

Atherosclerosis – progressive thickening and hardening of blood vessels

Basal Metabolic Rate – the amount of energy used by the body when at complete rest, following at least 12 hours of fasting, and in a normal environment. This is the minimum amount of energy required to maintain normal body processes

Beriberi – syndrome characterised by muscle weakness, loss of appetite, oedema, inflammation of nerves and heart disease

Bioavailable – the amount of a substance that can be absorbed, transported and utilised, following oral ingestion

Blood Pressure – the pressure exerted on the artery walls by the circulating blood. The measurement is usually in two sets of numbers. Systolic is the pressure exerted when the heart beats and the pressure is highest, whilst diastolic is measured between beats and pressure is lowest

Brassica Vegetables – genus of vegetables that includes broccoli, brussels sprouts, cabbage, cauliflower, kale, turnips

Bronchospasm – contraction of the smooth muscles of the bronchi and bronchioles, which causes a narrowing of the air passages

Calcific Urolithiasis – the formation of stones in the kidney, bladder and/or urethra

Cardiac arrhythmias – any abnormality or perturbation in the normal activation sequence of the heart (myocardium), possibly resulting from any of a number of conditions, and with the potential to negatively affect blood flow to the brain and other vital organs

Cardiomyopathy – 'heart muscle disease' – a condition that causes deterioration in the normal functioning of the heart, such as if the heart muscle becomes inflamed

Cardiovascular Disease – any abnormal condition characterised by a structural or functional disorder of the heart or blood vessels

Caries – commonly used term for the decay of teeth or bones

Cataracts – a clouding (opacity) of the lens of the eye, possibly leading to reduced vision or blindness

Cecum (or caecum) – the first portion of the large intestine

Chlorophyll – the group of green pigments found in photosynthetic organisms, such as plants and algae

Cholesterol – fatty substance (lipid) synthesised in the liver of animals. Humans both manufacture cholesterol and obtain it from the diet. Cholesterol is essential for the formation of cell membranes

Chronic Renal Insufficiency – the stage at which kidney function has decreased by more than half of normal levels

Coenzyme – a compound, usually containing a vitamin or mineral, which binds to a specific enzyme in order to activate it

Collagen – fibrous protein that is the basic building block of connective tissues

Colon – the part of the large intestine that extends from the caecum to the rectum

Colorectum – the distal 25 cm of the bowel, including the colon and rectum, regarded as a unit

Communicable Disease – an infectious disease that can be passed from one person to another

Convulsions – seizure, resulting in uncontrollable and rapid shaking, as muscles contract and relax repeatedly

Coprolites – fossilised faeces

196

Coronary Artery Disease (CAD) – usually caused by atherosclerosis, CAD is a condition in which plaques block the flow of blood to the heart

Coronary Heart Disease (CHD) – heart disease caused by narrowing of arteries that supply blood to the heart. The name is sometimes considered more generalised than CAD, as it can result from other causes

Corticosteriods – steroid hormones produced in the adrenal cortex

Cranium – the bones that make up the skull and protect the brain

Crocodilians – from the order *Crocodylia*, which includes alligators, caimans and crocodiles

Cruciferous Vegetables – named for their cross-shaped flowers, they include the sub-group of brassica vegetables, in addition to daikon, radish, watercress and wasabi. These vegetables are associated with the removal of toxic substances from the body

Cystic Fibrosis – inherited disease in which the internal organs are affected by the production of sticky mucus from their associated glands, leading to difficulties in breathing and digesting food

Dementia – Loss of mental abilities, including thinking, memory and reasoning, associated with damage to nerve cells in the brain

Dermatitis – Skin disease characterised by areas of itching, redness, scaling, inflammation and loss of the surface of the skin. Results from contact with irritant or allergen

Diabetes Mellitus – Disease caused by insufficiency or ineffectiveness of insulin, leading to chronically elevated blood glucose levels

Diverticulitis – Inflammatory condition of the pouches (diverticula) on the wall of the colon, which can lead to constant and severe pain, and an increase in infection

Dyskenisia / Dyskenesia – Difficulty in performing voluntary movements, often related to Parkinson's disease

Dyslipidaemia - elevated LDL cholesterol and triacylglycerides, with a reduced HDL cholesterol

Eczema – Chronic condition in which the skin may become itchy, reddened, dry, flaky and cracked

Electron – negatively-charged subatomic particle, found around the outside of atomic nuclei

Encephalisation – refers to the tendency for the brain size of a species to increase (or for neural and sensory organs to become more centralised) over evolutionary time

Endocrine – pertaining to hormones or the glands that secrete them

Enzymes – proteins that act as biochemical catalysts

Epidemiology – study of factors related to the health and disease of populations

Epithelium – the outside layer of cells that cover all surfaces of the body, including the skin, organs, cavities and glands.

Exfoliative Dermatitis (erythroderma) – inflammation of most, if not all, of the skin, which results in scaling

Exogenous – refers to substances originating outside of the body

Exudate – fluid with a high protein and/or debris content, which is deposited in tissues or on tissue surfaces, following injury or inflammation

Frugivores – Species that feeds primarily on fruits

Gallstone Disease – condition caused by stones that have formed in the gall bladder from cholesterol, bile salts and calcium. These can cause discomfort or severe pain following a meal

Gastrointestinal Reflux – caused when contents from the stomach splashes into the oesophagus, which can cause inflammation and damage

Gastrointestinal (G.I.) Tract – the passageway from the mouth to the anus in which food is broken down, absorbed, transported and waste products eliminated. The GI tract has a total length of approximately 9 metres (30 ft), and includes the oesophagus, stomach, and the small and large intestines.

Genotype – the genetic makeup of an individual/organism

Genus – the taxonomic category at the level below family and above species

Glaucoma – disease in which the pressure within the eye is sufficient to result in partial or complete loss of vision

Gout – inflammation caused by deposits of uric acid crystals in the joint space

Gracilisation – evolutionary process in which a more gracile (gracefully slender) structure is selected for

Haemoglobin – protein within erythrocytes (red blood cells) that transports oxygen and carbon dioxide in the blood

High Density Lipoproteins (HDL Cholesterol) – a substance that scavenges surplus cholesterol from the blood, and transports it to the liver

Herbivores – Species that feed primarily on plant foods

Hiatal Hernia – protrusion (herniation) of upper portion of stomach into the chest cavity, through an opening in the diaphragm called the oesophageal hiatus

Hormone – chemical substance produced by a gland or organ, which controls and regulates the activity of certain cells or organs

Hypercholesterolaemia – High levels of cholesterol in the blood

Hyperglycaemia – High levels of glucose in the blood

Hyperlipidaemia – High levels of fat (lipids) in the blood

Hyperosmolar – refers to an abnormally increased osmolar concentration of body fluids. Osmolar refers to the concentration of active particles within a solution, such as might pass through a semi-permeable membrane

Hyperpyrexia – Abnormally high temperature

Hypertension – High blood pressure

Hypertonic Dehydration (Hypernatraemic dehydration) – occurs when fluid lost from body contains less sodium than that found in the blood

Hypernatraemia – abnormally high levels of sodium in the blood

Hyponatraemia – abnormally low levels of sodium in the blood

Hypoplasia – Underdevelopment or incomplete development of an organ or part

Inflammatory Bowel Disease (IBD) – non-specific term for diseases that result in inflammation of the bowel (ulcerative colitis and Crohn's disease)

Insulin Resistance – condition in which a normal amount of insulin released into the blood is insufficient to elicit a normal response (i.e. to reduce blood glucose concentration to normal levels).

Invertebrate – organisms that do not have a backbone (spine)

Isotope – a chemical element with the same atomic number as another chemical element, but a different atomic mass

Ketoacidosis – occurs when high concentrations of ketone bodies accumulate in the blood, leading to ketosis and acidosis. Ketone bodies are substances made to break down fat when normal insulin is insufficient to break down glucose

Kidney Stones – mineral deposit that forms in the kidney

Large Intestine – section of intestine (gut) that extends from caecum to rectum

Low Density Lipoproteins (LDL Cholesterol) – lipoprotein that transports cholesterol in the blood. High concentrations are associated with increased risk of heart disease and atherosclerosis

Leukaemia – *lit. white blood* – cancer of the developing cells of the bone marrow. Should refer specifically to the leukocytes (white blood cells), but is often generalised to any cancer of the blood or bone marrow

Lipoprotein – Molecule of protein and fat (lipid), which transports cholesterol around in the blood

201

Lymph Nodes – filter the lymphatic fluid and can trap bacteria and cancers that would otherwise be travelling around the body

Lymphatic System – network of organs, lymph nodes, ducts and vessels that transport lymph around the body. Important for removal of waste that cannot pass from cells directly into circulation, and a key part of the immune system

Macronutrient – commonly thought of as the energy-providing nutrients (carbohydrates, protein and fats), they are essential nutrients required in relatively large amounts. Water and oxygen are sometimes included, as well as some minerals, such as calcium, sodium, phosphorous and chloride

Mammalia – class of warm-blooded vertebrates characterised by mammary glands in the females

Mandible – lower jawbone

Marrow – the vascular, fatty tissue that fills most bone cavities and where white and red blood cells and platelets are formed

Megaloblastic Anaemia – group of blood disorders characterised by larger than normal red blood cells, often with lower levels of white blood cells and platelets

Metabolism – commonly used to refer to the breakdown of food and its transformation into energy, but more appropriately refers to all biochemical processes within a living organism involving the building up (anabolism) and breaking down (catabolism) of substances.

Metastasis – transfer of disease from an organ or one part of the body to another (due to the transfer of cells or micro-organisms)

Micronutrient – a substance that is required in relatively small amounts for the survival and growth of an organism (i.e. most vitamins and minerals)

Mitral Valve Prolapse (MVP) – the mitral valve controls blood flow between the left atrium and left ventricle. An abnormality in the valve allows a prolapse back into the atrium, allowing a small amount of blood to sometimes pass back into the atrium from the ventricle

Myocardial Infarction (heart attack) – caused by blood clot that blocks a coronary (heart) artery, depriving the area beyond the clot of oxygen, leading to tissue death.

Myopia – (near- or short-sightedness) – results from a cornea that is too curved, or an eyeball that is too long. Distant objects appear blurred as a result

Nasopharyngeal Carcinoma – tumour arising from the epithelial cells of the nasopharynx, the uppermost region of the pharynx (throat)

Natural Selection – the process by which some species persist through time, whilst others become extinct or adapt. Natural selection is affected by the rates of reproduction versus rates of death

Neolithic - *Lit. New Stone Age* – characterised by primitive farming and the domestication of animals, along with the development of crafts and the making of polished stone tools. The period began around 10,000 BC in the Middle East, and from about 4000 BC in Europe

Neoplastic Disease – Abnormal and uncontrolled cell division

Nephrolithiasis – process of forming kidney stones

Nephropathy – kidney damage/disease, commonly associated with diabetes mellitus

Neural Tube Defects (NTDs) – defects of the foetal brain or spine. The neural tube is the structure from which the central nervous system develops

Neuroblastoma – malignant tumour that arises in immature nerve cells, affecting infants and children

Neurology – medical science concerned with diagnosis and treatment of disorders of the nervous system, including the brain, spinal cord and nerves

Neuropsychiatric – relating to both neurology and psychiatry

Neurotransmitter – chemical substance that transmits nerve impulses across a synapse (space between nerve cells)

Nitrate – salt or ester of nitric acid / nitrogen-containing compound, existing in either the atmosphere of as a dissolved gas in water

Oedema – swelling of tissue caused by excess accumulation of fluid

Oesophageal Adenocarcinoma – malignant tumour of the oesophagus, of glandular origin

Oesophagus – the passage/tube along which food travels between the throat and the stomach

Old World – Eastern Hemisphere of Europe, Asia and Africa

Oldowan Industry – earliest formally recognised tool-making tradition from the Lower Palaeolithic, dating to approximately two million years ago, and based upon stone tools found in Olduvai Gorge, amongst other places

Oligohydramnios – condition referring to having too little amniotic fluid in the womb. The amniotic fluid is necessary to protect the foetus and for proper growth and development

Omega-Six Fatty Acid – a type of essential fatty acid, required for good health, but which needs to be in a ratio of 4:1 or less to Omega three fatty acids. Omega six fatty acids are commonly obtained from vegetable oils

Omega-Three Fatty Acid – a type of essential fatty acid, found in high quantities in fish and seafood, as well as bone marrow and brain tissue. These fats are required by the brain and are associated with good cardiovascular health

Omnivores – species that eat both plant and animal foods

Oropharynx – area of the throat at the back of the mouth

Osteomalacia – generalised term referring to loss of skeletal bone mass due to demineralisation

Osteopenia – condition referring to lower than normal bone mineral density, but not low enough to be classed as osteoporosis

Osteoporosis (Brittle Bone Disease) – a decreased bone mineral density associated with an increased risk of fractures

Palaeolithic – *Oldest age of the stone* – from the first use of stone tools around two million years ago, until the end of the Pleistocene Epoch approximately 10,000 years ago.
It is subdivided according to developments in stone tool technology:
Lower Palaeolithic (Oldowan, Clactonian, Acheulean) ~2.5m to 250,000 years ago
Middle Palaeolithic (Mousterian) ~250,000 to 35,000 year ago
Upper Palaeolithic (Aurignacian, Grevattian) ~35,000 to 10,000 years ago

Pellagra – 'rough skin' – a disorder that causes a variety of symptoms affecting the skin, mucus membranes, central nervous system and gastrointestinal system. It is often associated with redness and swelling of the mouth and tongue, skin rash, diarrhoea, and mental problems such as memory loss. Pellagra can either be primary (related to niacin deficiency) or secondary (resulting from other disorders that affect niacin availability)

Phytoestrogens – plant-derived compounds with oestrogenic activity that can be obtained naturally from the diet

Pleistocene – The 'Great Ice Age' - 1.8 million to ~10,000 years ago
Early (Lower) Pleistocene: 1.8 million to 780,000
Middle Pleistocene: 780,000 to 130,000
Late (Upper) Pleistocene: 130,000–~10,000

Polycystic Kidney Disease – genetic disorder characterised by the formation of abnormal cysts in the kidneys

Polycystic Ovary Syndrome – hormonal disorder characterised by larger than average ovaries with an abnormally large number of cysts. Ovulation is typically rare, resulting in irregular periods and reduced fertility

Proteinuria – presence of an abnormal amount of protein in the urine

Resting Metabolic Rate – the amount of energy used by the body when at rest. A value calculated based upon this is often used in calorie-controlled diets, in order to ascertain the correct balance of energy ingested to energy expended. The resting metabolic rate is the normal representation of energy usage during the day, as opposed to basal metabolic rate, which requires less normal controls (RMR takes into account daily activity levels, thermogenesis, and thermoregulation, whereas BMR is concerned only with the minimal processes required for life).

Retinopathy – generalised term referring to a disease of the retina

Rhinitis – inflammation of the mucus membrane that lines the nose, usually the result of an allergen, and generally associated with the typical symptoms of a cold

Rickets – disease characterised by a failure to properly mineralise bone. This causes osteomalacia, leading to significant bending and distortion of bones

Sacculated Colon – refers to the shape of the colon, having saclike dilations or expansions

Skin Tags (Acrochordons) – benign skin growth, often appearing as tissue hanging from a stalk, commonly found around the armpits, eyelids, neck, groin and under skin folds

Small Intestine – the part of the digestive tract that extends from the stomach to the large intestine, comprising the duodenum, jejunum and ileum

Speciation – evolutionary process resulting in the development of a distinct new species from an existing one

Species – a taxonomic classification of related organisms capable of interbreeding and giving birth to fertile offspring

Stable Isotope – element that is not susceptible to radioactive decay

Stanols – naturally occurring chemicals found in plant foods, associated with reduced cholesterol levels

Steroid Hormones – structurally-related hormones derived from cholesterol, including testosterone, oestrogen, progesterone, which affect the growth and development of the sex organs and characteristics

Sterols – similar to stanols, sterols are chemicals found in plants that are associated with improved cholesterol profiles

Thromboembolism – formation of a clot (thrombus) in a blood vessel that is carried in the blood and plugs another vessel, such as within an organ or a limb, starving the area fed by that vessel of oxygen and causing local cell death (if this occurs in the heart or brain, then a myocardial infarction or stroke may result, potentially causing death)

Thyroid Gland – endocrine gland located in the neck and involved in the regulation of growth and metabolism, as well as heart rate, blood pressure and thermoregulation

Thyroid Goiter – abnormal enlargement of the thyroid gland

Tics – involuntary, repetitive and/or spasmodic muscle movements

Triacylglycerol (triacylglyceride, TAG) – naturally occurring ester of glycerol and three fatty acids. Most fats (lipids) are stored in the body as triacylglycerol and it is the main constituent of animal and vegetable fats

Urticaria (hives) – raised, red, itchy and possibly painful rash, usually associated with an allergic reaction

Vertebrate – animal with a spinal column (backbone)

Viscera – the internal organs of the body, especially those contained within the abdominal and thoracic cavities, including the intestines

Very Low Density Lipoproteins (VLDL Cholesterol) – type of cholesterol that transports triglycerides in the blood. VLDL is catabolised into intermediate-density lipoproteins and then to low-density lipoproteins, high levels of which are associated with an increased risk of heart disease

Appendix III

Index

Index

asparagus · 116, 120, 121, 126, 133
Aspartame · 164, 185, 189
atherogenic · 50, 59, 94, 96, 97, 178
atherosclerosis · 45, 54, 59, 113, 123, 136, 157, 197, 201
Australia · 61, 100
australopithecines · 20, 22, 24, 26, 27, 35, 76, 77, 81, 98, 167, 170
autoimmune diseases · 93
Avocados · 122, 130
axes · 29, 84

B

baboons · 80
bacteria · 10, 70, 107, 120, 127, 139, 140, 141, 142, 202
baked foods · 42, 92
bananas · 108, 111, 122, 130, 133
Barley · 100, 108
base · 77, 82, 144, 148, 170
beans · 14, 59, 71, 88, 103, 169, 182
beef · 64, 91, 120, 121, 122, 146
beef extract · 64
beefsteaks · 64

beers · 62, 69
benomyl · 163
Beriberi · 120, 195
berries · 14, 54, 100
beta-carotene · 137
bifidobacteria · 70, 140, 141, 142
Bifidobacterium longum · 143
bile acids · 101
Biotin · 59, 119
bipedal · 9, 19, 21, 78
birds · 8, 76, 99
biscuits · 42, 101, 111
black pepper · 126
bleeding gums · 117
bloating · 129
blood clotting · 93, 120, 125, 127, 160
blood plasma · 148
blood pressure · 13, 15, 39, 47, 49, 50, 54, 55, 56, 59, 67, 74, 89, 93, 99, 106, 125, 133, 134, 155, 157, 181, 182, 200, 208
BMI · 50, 51, 61
body fat · 15, 52, 67, 84, 90, 91, 105
body mass index · 50, 51, 61
bone · 28, 29, 37, 71, 81, 82, 84, 88, 117, 120, 123, 125, 127, 130, 131, 132, 142, 148, 156, 159, 171, 201, 202, 205, 207

bone formation · 125, 159
bone loss · 127, 130
bone mineral density · 89, 125, 130, 205
bone pain · 117, 132
bonobos · 16, 32, 102
bowel cancer · 159
brain · 18, 20, 28, 34, 35, 37, 73, 74, 82, 87, 98, 99, 118, 122, 148, 155, 165, 171, 176, 178, 182, 184, 195, 197, 198, 204, 205, 208
breads · 41, 42, 62, 69, 144
breakfast cereals · 42
breastfeeding · 37, 149
breastmilk · 140
breathing problems · 132
broccoli · 116, 119, 120, 121, 122, 123, 133, 195
bronchospasm · 165
brussels sprouts · 106, 117, 120, 121, 123, 195
buds · 26, 32
Bulgaria · 53
butter · 91, 93, 134
butylated hydroxyanisole · 164

C

cabbage · 106, 108, 125, 133, 195
caffeine · 151, 154, 155, 156, 157, 176, 177, 180, 181, 183, 189
cakes · 42, 101, 102
calcium · 34, 45, 71, 88, 102, 116, 118, 125, 127, 129, 132, 139, 144, 145, 150, 156, 160, 199, 202
calcium regulation · 118
cancer · 10, 13, 31, 45, 49, 50, 60, 61, 62, 63, 64, 65, 66, 74, 94, 98, 113, 114, 115, 118, 123, 133, 139, 141, 142, 152, 159, 160, 164, 172, 176, 178, 179, 180, 181, 182, 183, 184, 185, 186, 187, 188, 189, 190, 191, 192, 201
Cantaloupe · 111
carbohydrates · 54, 63, 77, 81, 96, 97, 104, 105, 110, 113, 119, 121, 122, 126, 142, 150, 163, 169, 192, 202
carbon · 22, 24, 150, 184, 199

carbon dioxide · 22, 150, 199
carcasses · 28, 80, 82, 90
carcinogens · 62, 63, 64, 65, 141, 169
cardiac arrhythmias · 54, 132-133, 157
cardiomyopathy · 133
cardiovascular disease · 46, 53, 105, 119, 142
cardiovascular disorders · 160
cardiovascular health · 159, 161
cardiovascular system · 53, 120, 146
caries · 41
carmoisine · 164
carnivores · 24, 25, 28, 32, 80, 85, 90
carotenoids · 59, 137
carrots · 108, 116, 122
cartilage · 117
cats · 28, 81
cauliflower · 106, 117, 120, 131, 195
cecum · 31, 34, 201
Celery · 108
cell division · 116, 123, 135, 203
cell formation · 121
cell membranes · 95, 96, 119, 130, 137, 196
cellulose · 100, 107
cereal · 39, 40, 42, 105, 107, 108, 109,

112, 113, 144, 169, 182
Cereal grains · 144
cereals · 41, 59, 71, 100, 111, 144, 169
cerebrospinal fluid · 148
cervix · 65
cheese · 62, 69, 71, 91, 93, 134, 146
chemistry · 22
chemotherapy · 65
Cherries · 111
chicken · 122
Chickpeas · 129
childbirth · 140
childhood · 41, 118, 136, 146, 147, 154, 163, 166, 190
children · 20, 34, 37, 49, 50, 67, 77, 78, 97, 127, 135, 140, 146, 149, 150, 152, 157, 164, 165, 166, 190, 204
chimpanzees · 16, 27, 32, 76, 77, 80, 102
chlorophyll · 65
chocolate · 42, 151, 154
cholesterol · 13, 47, 50, 53, 54, 55, 56, 57, 58, 73, 88, 92, 93, 94, 95, 96, 97, 105, 109, 112, 113, 117, 126, 127, 128, 135, 136, 155, 160, 192, 196,

fluid consumption ·
148
Fluoride · 127
folate · 34, 61, 65,
123, 180, 184
Food additives · 163
food availability · 10,
27, 41, 52
food chain · 43, 115,
142
food dressings · 42
Food intolerances ·
146
forage · 10
foraging · 36, 76, 100
forests · 18, 20, 26, 32,
43, 101, 167
fossil record · 19
fractures · 13, 71, 88,
117, 156, 159, 180,
205
free radicals · 69, 136,
137, 138
fructose · 101, 113
frugivores · 168
frugivorous · 19
fruits · 12, 14, 18, 19,
26, 32, 33, 39, 46, 53,
54, 56, 62, 64, 65, 69,
71, 76, 89, 100, 101,
102, 103, 105, 106,
107, 108, 109, 112,
114, 117, 137, 138,
144, 146, 149, 161,
169, 170, 171, 176,
199

G

gallbladder disease ·
50
gallstone disease · 152
Garlic · 108
gastric
adenocarcinoma · 137
gastric cancer · 64,
114
gastrointestinal reflux ·
109
gastrointestinal tract ·
146, 148, 154
genera · 18, 78, 141,
170
genes · IX, 12, 16, 17,
19, 187
genome · 16, 17, 39,
41, 143, 169, 170, 177
genotype · IX, X, 12,
168, 172
Germany · 29
Ghee · 54
Ginger · 108, 130
glaucoma · 152
global cooling · 22, 23
glucose · 37, 47, 49,
50, 56, 67, 88, 101,
104, 105, 110, 112,
113, 119, 126, 130,
134, 179, 197, 200,
201
glucose intolerance ·
132
glucose tolerance ·
105, 126

glucosinolates · 103
glutamine · 45
glutathione · 45, 181
glycaemic index · 110,
190
glycaemic load · 67,
97, 105, 110, 112, 113,
190, 192
goats · 40
gorillas · 27, 32, 102
gout · 47, 112, 131
gracilisation · 26
grains · 14, 39, 40, 42,
105, 107, 108, 109,
113, 144, 152, 169
grapefruit · 130, 133
grapes · 100
grasses · 76
grassland · 22
grazing animals · 80
Great Britain · 61
Greeks · 31
green tea · 120
gut flora · 69, 70, 139

H

habitat · 17, 24
habits · 14, 26, 36, 45,
47, 112, 152, 155, 161
haemoglobin · 122,
129, 194
haemorrhoids · 109
hair loss · 119, 135,
166

I

216

220

223